CHOOSING **WEIGHT**

CHOOSING WEIGHT

INTENTIONALLY

How to Lose and Gain Weight Without Dieting

XANDRIA WILLIAMS

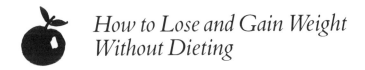

CHARLES LETTS
Letts
of London®
FOUNDED 1796

Dedication

This book is dedicated to my patients and the workshop participants who gave freely of themselves, thereby offering the examples that are shared here with you the reader.

Published in the UK in 1992 by
Charles Letts & Co Ltd,
Letts of London House,
Parkgate Road,
London SW11 4NQ

First published in Australasia in 1990 by
Simon & Schuster Australia,
7 Grosvenor Place, Brookvale,
NSW 2100

© 1990 Xandria Williams

The author can be contacted care of the publishers.
Charles Letts & Co Ltd

A CIP catalogue record for this book is available from the British Library

'Letts' is a registered trademark of Charles Letts & Co Limited

Printed in the United Kingdom

CONTENTS

PREFACE

It is important that I give you some background to this book, to tell you how the ideas were developed and how it came to be written.

It all started with a patient in the clinic, who was not even overweight. This woman, Jennifer, had been to see me suffering from thrush. I had advised her what she should do and she had left promising to put the treatment into action. Now, two years later, she was back again with the same problem. She recalled her treatment exactly, yet she had not carried it out. Instead she had put up with the problem for several months. I wanted to know why.

Jennifer was married to Roger and they had two children. Marital relations were strained yet Jennifer could not walk out, she was terrified of being a single parent with two small children and minimal financial resources.

Roger still expected sex. Jennifer was definitely not interested. Yet each time she refused and Roger became angry she feared that they would say critical things and the marriage would end in separation or divorce. Then Jennifer got thrush. Wonderful, she now had a valid physical reason for avoiding intercourse.

For the first month, Jennifer kept saying she would go to see someone about her problem as soon as she had time. However, the children needed attention and there was just so much to do.

Then this wore a bit thin, Roger became impatient and chivied her into getting something done. By then it was school holidays and there was even more to do. Finally, she could think of no more reasons to avoid a consultation so she reluctantly arrived in my clinic. Was it possible that she had been trying to avoid a cure?

We decided the time had come for her to go away and think about things. She agreed to follow the treatment that I had suggested and to come back in a week's time. She left, but as she walked down the street all the old defences came up. She found herself saying "How dare she say I was using the situation . . . " etc. and she resolved not to come back. Then after a few more days of thought she decided she would return after all.

At the next consultation she said "You know, I was sure in my mind that you would say that it was more serious this time, and that I would find that what you prescribed didn't really work. In fact that was what I was really hoping would happen. Then I could have gone home still with the problem and postponed dealing with the situation."

We did a lot of work on her attitudes and emotional reactions to Roger and to her home life. The outcome was good. Her marriage improved and she could afford to live without the thrush.

This set me thinking back to many patients' stories in which their emotional and mental needs were closely tied to their physical problems. As a result the workshop Choosing Health Intentionally (CHI) was written.

Soon after the CHI workshop was started it became obvious that the thoughts and attitudes that affect your health also play an enormous role in your size and shape, the clothes you wear, your grooming etc. The outcome was the Choosing Weight Intentionally (CWI) workshop, on which this book is based.

This is a very practical book and so it must be if you are to achieve the results you want. It is all too easy to simply read a book and leave it at that. But to change your weight and the way you look, you must act on the ideas you find here, even if it is all or largely done inside your head. You will be asked to do a number of things as we move through the pages together. Please do them. There is nothing to be achieved by getting through this book in a day.

From years of using the ideas presented here both in my office and in workshops, it has been shown that they work. All that is required from you is a willingness to work with them and do everything that is asked of you with full commitment and honesty. No-one else can lose or gain weight for you. No-one else can delve inside you to find old memories that have dictated the way you lead your life nor can they change the way you react to situations today. No-one else can face up to your fears, for it can sometimes be scary to face memories you have learned to bury and the possible truths you have come to dread.

Furthermore, no-one else may ever know if you are fooling yourself when you insist that things are the way you want them to be. If you pretend, you will be the loser and the struggle with your weight will continue.

Only you can solve your weight problems. So, if you're ready, let's go.

INTRODUCTION

OVERWEIGHT

So you want to lose weight. Is this the first time you have tried or has it been an ongoing process? Have you tried to lose weight in the past but failed? Have you lost weight successfully and felt proud of yourself only to put all or part of it back again when you came off the diet? Have you lost some weight, plateaued and given up in disgust or cut down on your calories even further only to find you could lose no more even when you cut everything in half? Have you started on a diet with the best of intentions and then found yourself bingeing on a favourite food or at a social function and given up, saying you'd start again tomorrow? Join the club; this is true for half the population or more.

Do you start on a diet and do well for a few days and then find something happens that upsets you and head for the fridge or the cookie jar? Or perhaps something good happens and you feel you must eat and drink to celebrate. Or perhaps you are tense before a special event and feel you must eat to reassure yourself. Join the club; you are one of the emotional eaters.

Do you tell yourself that you can have just one chocolate chip cookie and then find you have eaten the entire packet? Do you stay off chocolate for days and then suddenly eat a whole block? Do you suddenly crave peanut butter sandwiches, caramel milk shakes or cheesecake and ice cream? You are an addict and so are half of all overweight people.

Do you keep saying to people that you can't understand why you're overweight, that you only eat the tiniest meals? But do you, in fact, eat the largest number of snacks, picking up this and that to nibble all day long when you are bored or faced with a task you don't relish? Join nibblers anonymous for they are indeed anonymous, even to themselves. Few nibblers realise just how much they eat, as if by not calling it a meal, not sitting down to eat it or not putting it on a plate but directly into the mouth, it doesn't count as food.

Maybe other people think you should lose weight but you don't really want to? Perhaps it's your husband or wife who thinks you should be slimmer, a parent, child or friend that is urging you to start. Perhaps you are content to be the weight you are, but think you ought to lose weight because everyone else thinks so. Maybe all your family is overweight and you reassure yourself that is the way you are meant to be and that no diet would be successful anyway, and yet you still find there are times when you wish you were slimmer?

If any of the above is true, then this book will help you discover ways to lose weight without dieting, without deprivation and without willpower. Losing weight the *Choosing Weight Intentionally* way is losing weight the easy way. Yet sometimes the easy way is a challenge and may occasionally prove a little difficult. However, the challenge will not be in relation to the food you eat or don't eat.

UNDERWEIGHT

So you want to gain weight. Are you described as skinny behind your back? If you turn sideways, do you fail to cast a shadow? Have you eaten until you are full and then more only to leap on the scales the next morning to find there has been no change? The overweight do just the opposite, you know. They step ever so gingerly onto the scales, hoping to fool the dial into stopping a little sooner on its way up.

Do you find food boring, tasteless and a waste of time? Do you feel that everything you eat simply goes straight through you? Do you long for the muscles and curves of your heavier friends? Or perhaps you are content with the way you are and yet other people tell you to gain some weight. You get very little sympathy from your overweight friends, or even from your normal-weight friends, since most of them are conscious of the discipline needed to lose weight or stay slim. Anyone who is overweight thinks it would be wonderful to have your problem. Yet, it is often harder for you to gain a few extra kilograms than for others to lose a few. Did you pick up this book, thinking, from the title, that it could be related to the underweight as well as the overweight?

If you answer yes to any of these questions, then this book is for you, because this book is about changing your weight if you want to. It is about choosing the weight you want to be and reaching and maintaining it. Inevitably, the book focuses mainly on those that are overweight, and the majority of examples are about them. However, the real issues are your mental programming about diet, food, meal-times and so forth. All you need to do is translate the overweight examples into underweight examples. I beg your forbearance in this but it is not easy to include many under-weight stories since less people are troubled by this prob-lem. You will, of course, find some examples that are directly related to being underweight.

The main aim is to explore yourself and your attitudes and to discover how they affect your body weight and shape. You can do this every bit as well as the overweight.

Overweight or underweight — whatever it is you are, you are about to embark on a voyage of discovery about your-self, your past and your emotional responses to people and situations. You will learn how you use food and why. The method will work if you do. You may not believe all you read; you may not feel that it will work for you. But if you persist, if you are honest with yourself, if you do the mental exercises asked of you, you will indeed reach your desired weight — the weight you truly want to be.

Throughout this book the term "slim" is used to indicate appropriate weight and the term "thin" is used for the underweight.

THE RATIONALE FOR WEIGHT CHANGES

There are many reasons for not wanting to be underweight or overweight. Some of them relate to health, others are emotional and others relate to social causes and socially acceptable ideas.

Firstly, we will consider some health reasons for not being too fat or too thin. We will start with the heart since half to two-thirds of the population die of heart and cardiovascular related problems. If you took the total length of all the blood vessels, arteries, veins and capillaries in one pound of flesh and laid them end to end, how far do you think they would stretch? One yard? One mile? No, conservatively about 500 miles! That's a lot of extra pumping for the heart to do if you are overweight, and that's just in *one* extra pound of flesh. Clearly the heart is interested in having you slim. Overweight people are more likely to have a stroke, become diabetic and have more health problems than their slim counterparts.

Your weight affects your physical activity. Slim people can *do* more. They can play more sport, exercise more, move their bodies better and are more supple. Many overweight people are ashamed to be seen in a swimsuit and miss out on the fun of summers on the beach or around the pool. They are conscious of the way they look when they run, jog or play sport and so neglect such activities. Thin people, on the other hand, miss out on many sporting activities due to lack of muscle tone and strength. They, too, may be ashamed to be seen in a bikini or briefs since they feel they are all angles and bones.

The very overweight can experience inconveniences such as being unable to buy clothes that fit or finding that chairs or seats on buses or planes are too small and crowded for them. The very thin may also have trouble finding flattering clothes that fit. Thin ones can find chairs uncomfortable since they lack the appropriate padding.

If you are overweight, do you feel guilty? Many people

do. Some people even try to lose weight not because they *want* to but because they feel they *ought* to, and they feel guilty if they don't. They think, if they say they are *trying* to lose weight, this might lessen some of the real or imagined criticism.

It is often thought that slim people are happier, more successful and more popular than fat people. If you think this, you may be caught in a double bind. When you are unhappy you will want to lose weight and become slim. Yet many people, when they are unhappy, eat as a form of comfort. This is a no-win situation.

In a society where slim people are admired, there is pressure put on overweight people to lose the excess pounds. Gone are the days of Rubens and the cherubs, of curvaceous beauties with folds and dimples. In the twentieth century, the focus is on being slim — even thin. Slim women have an amazing selling power as we can see in advertisements of them draped over cars and washing machines, modelling clothes, demonstrating gadgets and equipment. Slim men are also in demand: you don't see fat men riding off into the sunset in advertisements. Magazines never stop telling you about the advantages of being slim. If you aren't, they warn you could lose your lover, your job, or your self-esteem. Almost every issue of a woman's magazine carries still another magical "sure-to-work" diet. The slim woman gets her man. The fat woman misses out. If a young woman wants to be sought after, she will endeavour to be slim. Slim girls have all the fun.

Being thin is less of a social hazard then being fat. Yet I meet many thin men who are convinced their sexual prowess and their appeal to the opposite sex would increase if only they could gain some weight. Wanting to lose weight is not the same thing as wanting to be slim. Conversely, wanting to be slim is not the same thing as wanting to lose weight. For most people the process of losing weight is one of deprivation and missed enjoyment. How can you convince your subconscious that this is what you want?

If, on the other hand, you focus on *wanting to be slim,*

ah, now that is something that you and your subconscious can both enjoy. Try it for yourself next time you decide to eat less. Focus your mind on being slim rather than on the process of losing weight. You may find it a whole lot easier to go without those extra mouthfuls. Conversely, if you find eating a bore, it will be hard to convince your subconscious that you want to gain weight. You will have a better chance of convincing it that you want to have a better or fuller figure.

THE RATIONALE FOR STAYING AS YOU ARE

It may be that staying fat or staying thin has advantages. Until you can identify these and deal with them, trying to lose or gain weight is like trying to climb a mountain with a ball and chain attached to your leg. You may want to find other ways of getting some of these benefits; you may want to grow beyond them and stop needing them.

Here are some reasons to stay fat or to stay thin given by people in my office or in the workshops. Many of them apply to being underweight as well as being overweight:

- You want to be safe and less attractive to the opposite sex — (a very common one).
- You hope people won't expect much of you.
- Your mother gets upset when you don't eat so you eat to please her.
- You're afraid of change.
- You fear that people can get too close to you when you get slim; your boundaries change.
- You prove that you're not perfect.
- You show that you put other people's needs such as your family's ahead of your own.
- You have a reason to criticise yourself.
- You have something to blame for other problems in your life.
- You can prove you were brought up badly.

- You get sympathy and attention when you discuss your problem.
- Talking about diets and food is easier than talking about more serious subjects.
- Talking about diets is a way to talk about yourself.
- You can feel helpless and dependent.
- You want to be soft and cuddly.

We talked before about some of the disadvantages of being too slim. Let's consider these further, both in the light of the Skinnies who want to gain weight and from the point of view of the Overweight who try to reduce excessively.

When you lose an excessive amount of weight, you lose fat. Some of this fat is the excess stored on buttocks, thighs, hips and belly and you don't need it. But there is also protective fat around important organs such as the kidneys, the liver and the heart. If you lose this protection, these organs could be damaged. Fat is also part of your temperature-control mechanism. It is harder for a thin person to maintain body heat in a cold climate than for a fat one to do so. Conversely, it is harder for a fat person to stay cool in a hot climate than a slim person. Your fat stores are also a source of energy. If you have too little fat you would be the first in trouble if you were cast away on a desert island. What about cuddles? It's all very well to admire the lack of bulges and creases on a slim sexy woman in a photo, but how much fun is it to hug a bag of bones whose sharp edges are likely to do damage? I happened to be on an ocean liner's maiden voyage. To publicise this we carried four stunning models who put on a show at each port of call, and also appeared at meals in an endless array of gorgeous gowns. When the weather became warm, I observed them one morning lying around the pool. Stripped of their beautiful clothes they were not just slim but seemed to be all bones.

Could you be wanting to be too slim? After all, the model's role is to display the clothes, not be seen for herself.

She is really a type of human coat hanger. Do you really want to be that slim, to disappear?

Some of the reasons for being too slim that have come up in my office and in the workshops include the following:

- If being slim is good, then being even thinner must be better;
- To be invisible;
- To avoid growing up;
- So that less is expected of me;
- So other people will protect me;
- So that people won't fight with me.

Before you start, be sure that you really want to lose or gain weight, as opposed to thinking you ought to, or trying to do it to please someone else. Also, be sure that your aim is one that is physiologically sensible.

PART ONE:
BASICS

REALISTIC CHANGES

So you think you want to lose weight. But do you? Even as I ask the question I can hear howls of protest. Of course you do. Isn't that why you picked up this book? Who wants to be fat? Haven't you been struggling to lose weight for ages? Yes, but do you *really* want to lose it? Let me tell you about Narelle.

Narelle came to see me because she was overweight. In fact she weighed 83 kilograms (13 stone). Her target weight was 58 kilograms (9 stone). She told me about all the diets she had tried and failed but insisted that she was now truly desperate and determined to lose weight and look better. The next step was for us to plan a regime that she could stick to and that would work for her.

A week later Narelle came back and got onto the scales and I said "Great, you have lost one-and-a-half kilograms (3 pounds). Isn't that good". I looked up to find that tears were running down her cheeks. The scales were put away and we sat down to talk.

Narelle's mother was Italian and when she was only sixteen she had fallen pregnant to her Norwegian boyfriend. Narelle was the result and had inherited her father's looks — blond with a heavy bone structure. Subsequently, her mother married a man who was Italian like herself who never fully accepted the illegitimate Narelle. The couple then had two other children — slim, dark, Italian and attractive. In 1960 when Narelle was born, an illegitimate child was a dreadful thing. Because of her illegitimacy and her blond colouring, she felt an outcast in the family. Her mother felt defensive and guilty about her and kept trying to push her into the background, and her father was irritated by her. A phrase that stuck in her mind was her mother's "Never mind about Narelle, she's big enough and fat enough to look after herself". This had been repeated so often that Narelle came to believe it.

When we sought the reason for her tears after a weight

loss of one and a half kilograms (3 pounds), she found that, deep down, she believed that if she lost weight and improved her looks she would no longer be able to look after herself. Only after a lot of work on her self-esteem and in changing her belief system could she comfortably and safely lose weight.

Here was the reason for her failures in the past. Every time she had lost weight to the point of fear, she had sabotaged the effort by bingeing on chocolate. Yet, they were really successes because she had maintained herself in a state in which she felt safe and able to deal with her life.

Now, you may well be saying that this has nothing to do with you as you had no such early patterning. You may have come from a warm and loving family. You may have been slim, competent, popular, with lots of friends. This was the case with Rosemary.

Rosemary had had a succession of boyfriends and her family had expected her to wed a handsome, successful extrovert who would fit into her social circle. Instead, she chose a quiet, thoughtful accountant. Within a few years her weight started to go up and when she came to see me she had 20 kilograms (3 stone) to lose. Like Narelle, Rosemary had tried many diets and always failed. However, she recognised that every time she lost a few kilograms she began to feel anxious, although she did not know why. She was keen to explore the reasons.

Her quiet and thoughtful accountant had seemed to her, when she first met him, to offer the security and peace missing from her hectic lifestyle. For the first two or three years she had revelled in this but then had come to realise that was all there was. He was unlikely to go much further in his profession or increase his income and while she still loved him, she also longed for more excitement in her life. She began to feel restricted and so it was agreed she should go back to her work in marketing. This meant that her husband felt increasingly inadequate about his inability to provide socially or financially, jealous of all the men she worked with and fearful of losing her. It was at about this time Rosemary's weight started to increase.

We discovered, then, that she was afraid to lose weight because this would increase the chances of men wishing to have affairs with her. Not only that, but she was afraid that she would be tempted to accept such offers for the excitement and piquancy they would offer even though she did not wish to jeopardise her marriage or hurt her husband. It was safer to hide behind her extra 20 kilograms (3 stone) and not be tempted into something she might regret.

These issues do not only involve women. Men, too, have their weight problems and hang-ups. George was such a man.

George was overweight but this had not bothered him until he went to his doctor for one of his regular checkups. As usual, his doctor told him that he should lose weight and this had been an ongoing discussion for years with no expectation of change on either side. The doctor had little hope that George would change his lifestyle, stop his business lunches, cut down on beer and wine, do any exercise or even eat less at each meal. Yet, he felt it his duty to keep mentioning it would be a good idea. George had become so used to the doctor's comments that he hardly heard them. He certainly gave them no thought except perhaps to sigh and regretfully pat his paunch, saying "What the hell!"

But this time was different because the doctor told George that his blood pressure was up, his cholesterol and triglyceride levels were high, he was over forty, overweight, over-stressed and a candidate for a heart attack. This made George think and listen, then finally agree that something should be done.

George appeared in my office and we organised an eating and exercise programme. After three weeks of steady weight-loss he was nearly five kilograms (10 pounds) lighter and things seemed to be going well. Then the weight-loss stopped. Three more weeks went by with little change except that he even gained a few kilograms.

The time had come to find out what was going on. George still professed himself to be keen to lose weight and get fit. He insisted he was sticking to the programme that he was walking more and climbing stairs but the weight stayed there. He said that he had been under a lot of stress, that he had been feeling anxious, and that there was a major company project coming off shortly. Since he had raised this issue, it seemed a good idea to explore it.

George worked with a firm of architects and was excellent at his work. He was wonderful with individual clients. He could sit down with any of them and create the concept he had for an office, a shopping complex, a holiday resort. He could do all that was necessary to get his staff to bring about the desired result. Just one thing terrified him — the thought of standing up in front of a group of people to give a formal presentation of his ideas. In the past he had always been able to claim his weight and his appearance as a reason to stay in the background. After all, he argued, his work was in the luxury class where elegance and beauty were critical. No-one wanted to see a fat man give the presentation; it should be one of the younger, slimmer, more elegant men that did that. On this basis he had stayed in the background for most of his career and was known as the backroom brain, praised for being generous enough to allow other men to demonstrate his work.

Now, things were changing. A 5 kilogram (10 pound) loss was not all that much as he still had many kilograms to go. But suddenly he realised that he, too, could become slim and look elegant. This raised the spectre that he might have to get up on stage and perform the publicity part of his job. No, he thought, "not that". It was much safer to stay fat and risk a heart attack.

Again, the way to solve the weight problem was to solve the emotional problem. As we explored the reasons why George hated to talk in public we were gradually able to resolve them. George's partner was brought into the situation and it was explained that George had to lose weight for his health's sake but he still didn't want to speak in public until he was ready to do so. His partner agreed not to apply this pressure and, as a result, George was able to continue losing weight. In time, he may become comfortable making speeches.

So far we have discussed people who are overweight. *Choosing Weight Intentionally* is not only about the Overweight; it is also about the Underweight. They, too, have a weight problem, and, as indicated earlier, it's no good the Fatties saying "Oh yes, tell me about it, I'll happily swap problems any day", the Skinnies have just as serious a problem as the Fatties and it can cause just as much distress.

Maureen was only sixteen when her parents persuaded her to see me. At the time she was 1.7m (5 foot 6) but weighed only 45 kilograms (7 stone). When we met I realised she was anxious that she would get too fat rather than anxious about staying too thin.

Maureen was the youngest of five children and had come late in her parents' lives. Since there were several years between her and the older children, she had been much petted and fussed over by the rest of the family. As if to reinforce this view of herself, she was the last one in her class to start her periods and this meant she was "growing up". She had always been slim and short for her age until the last eighteen months when she'd had a growth spurt. Since her major claim to fame so far had been that of being small and being the baby in the family, growing up was a terrifying thought. Her reaction was to stay a child and the one thing she could control was her body weight; she could keep her body small by under-eating. Then, to her delight, she found this had another benefit when her periods stopped and she could again revert to feeling she was a child.

The problem with Maureen's solution was that she was seriously undermining her health. She was risking her health by using her body as a tool to deal with her unresolved emotional problems of identity and her fear that she would no longer be loved once she was an adult among adults.

This is a fairly typical case of anorexia nervosa and we worked on it accordingly. There are, however, many other cases of people being too slim although not anorexic.

Edward is a case in point. He came to see me because he was underweight and he wanted to gain some extra kilograms to look better. When someone wants to gain weight, it is important for health as well as cosmetic reasons that they gain muscle or protein bulk and not fat. To this end we planned Edward's diet carefully. In the first two weeks he gained one and a half kilograms (3 pounds) but then he stayed there. Again the time had come to explore the possibility of subconscious motives. He offered several reasons including increased activity at work, stress, and being too busy to eat but none of them really were adequate.

Edward had not always been thin. At school he had been one of the plumper boys. Then came college which he enjoyed. He was a quiet chap and preferred the peace of the library rather than the noise of a pub. Then there was the research for his Ph.D. on an abstruse topic, one that interested only him, his supervisor and a limited number of colleagues. Since funds were short he had to complete his thesis as fast as possible and had little time or opportunity for outside interests. He lived at home, and had not had to cope with the practical mechanics of living. Problems started for Edward when he began his first job where he was hailed as the expert on his particular subject. But here was a whole new adult world, one that he had entered at the late age of twenty-four. Suddenly he was supposed to know how to handle his taxes, how to manage his finances, find a home, find a wife, look after his affairs, and "be a man". Because he was tall, well-built and looked mature, he was assumed to be "a man of the world". His parents added to this by taking the view that they had supported him all this time and now it was their turn to lean on him, ask his advice and expect practical help.

It was all too much for Edward. He went for a holiday overseas and when he returned he had lost a lot of weight. Many people, especially his mother, made a fuss of him; he was so thin, he was so tired; they mustn't impose on him. Without realising it, he came to equate being thin with people expecting less of him. For the next ten years he was as thin as a rake, looking positively gaunt. By the time he was thirty-seven, the subconscious belief that any increase in his size would increase other people's expectations of him was so deeply ingrained that he found it almost physically impossible to increase the amount he ate. Now he had found he could actually add on one-and-a-half kilograms (3 pounds) and might indeed, horror of horrors, be able to gain even more weight. So there it was — the silent sabotage. Once this was realised and dealt with, Edward was able to gain 12.5 kilograms (2 stone) and look and feel good about it.

Martin was another slim man. He had always had trouble gaining weight and had stopped trying. Now he was about to get married and his girlfriend insisted that a scarecrow could not look good in a dinner suit. What was he to do? He explained that he didn't like eating nor did he want to spend time cooking larger meals. After some discussion we worked out a programme with which he seemed happy. This included adding a rich drink to the end of each meal, consisting of a powder-based supplement in milk or fruit juice.

All went well for a while but then the weight-gain stopped. I found that he had begun to replace some of his meals with the drink rather than add it to the meals. His first explanation was that he didn't have time to prepare meals. When we delved into it further we found that he had been overweight at his first school and had been taunted by the older boys. Then, in adolescence he thinned down to his present figure. As soon as he started to gain weight he became afraid that he would gain too much and be laughed at again.

Many of you will be starting to feel some form of empathy for Narelle or Rosemary, George or Edward or Martin. You may be starting to get some idea of why you have chosen to be the weight you are. Some of you may think that this approach is all very well for some people but that none of it relates to you. In time you may discover that it does, but this may not be readily apparent. There is much exploration ahead.

Some of you may feel put out by the ideas given so far. You could be thinking that, in your case, your weight has nothing to do with your emotions and it is not your fault or of your choosing that you are overweight or underweight; it is all to do with your glands and your metabolism. It will presumably be very satisfying for you if you can prove this and disprove the ideas given here. On the other hand, think how exciting it will be if you can be shown a way around the problem of your glands and metabolism, to a new slim you.

YOUR PRESENT CHOICE

Let's get back to thinking about your weight. Do you really want to lose or gain weight? Could it be that you are exactly the weight you want to be? Could it be that you have actually chosen to be your present weight? "No", you cry, "I do *not* want to be this weight. I would much rather be this or that much lighter or heavier. Think about it for a moment. If you stopped eating altogether you would eventually be a bag of bones. This is true even if the problem *does* have something to do with your glands and your metabolism.

This means that what you weigh now does have *something* to do with the amount you have eaten and drunk in the past. It has also had something to do with the amount of food energy you have chosen to burn up in exercise and other activities. What you have eaten and have drunk and how much energy you have burnt up has resulted from a thousand small decisions you have made over the past months and years. You chose to eat that chocolate, that extra potato, that large bowl of muesli, a big meal instead of a small one. It was more important, at that particular time, to eat the extra food than it was to abstain and be lighter. The weight you are now is the sum total of the various choices that went into the decision-making processes. Thus, you *are* the weight you have chosen to be. The same is true if you are too thin. You made the decision not to eat that one more mouthful, not to have that second helping, to skip those meals when you couldn't be bothered to eat.

Once you get hold of that thought you can get a grip on your so-called weight problem. You might even call it a weight-solution to any other problem with which you are grappling.

If you think this approach covers only a small part of your particular problem, so be it. At least it is one more tool to add to your armory in the fight against being over-weight or underweight. If you think this could be a major part of the problem, think how much easier sensible eating and steady weight loss or gain will become in the future. You *can* unravel the emotional entanglements that are associated with your eating patterns, your self-image, and the way you look. You *can* accept full responsibility for each eating decision you make and you can take the long-term view of what you are doing. You *can* get back conscious control of your weight and change your mind about the weight you want to be. You can come to *really* want to be the weight you have been *thinking* you want to be.

Once you accomplish this, losing weight or gaining weight will be easy.

DISCOVERING YOURSELF

Who are you? Who do you *think* you are? How would you describe yourself? Before you turn to the next page, get a pen and paper and describe yourself as you would to a stranger at the other end of the telephone. Think hard. Fill in all the details and give that stranger a description of who you are.

What did you write? Did you describe yourself in terms of your physical appearance? Was your job or what you do high on the list of descriptions? How did you identify yourself? Think now about the significance of this description in terms of your weight.

As you are reading this book, you are probably conscious about your weight and your appearance. If that is so, you probably described yourself in terms of the way you think you look. In a recent workshop I asked the participants to write down a description of themselves and this is what resulted. There were descriptions such as "I'm tall, overweight, with blond hair", "I'm short, fat, dark-haired with pimples and frown lines", "I'm skinny but with fat thighs", "I've got blue eyes and no bust", "I'm tall and all knobs and bones" and so on. Most people emphasised their size and shape over and above other aspects of themselves.

The way you eat or don't eat, the way you lose weight or stay fat, stay as you are or change your looks commonly relates to the mental image you have of yourself. If you persist in seeing yourself as fat and unattractive, then that is the way you are likely to stay.

This was Betty's experience. Ever since childhood, she had thought of herself as Big Bad Betty. As a child she was always getting into trouble and her mother would say "Oh, Betty you are bad. You've done so-and-so again and I've told you not to". As she grew older, her body increased in size and seemed to become ungainly and get too big for her to control. She became clumsy, knocking things over, bumping into things and bruising herself, spilling or dropping things or falling and grazing her legs. Then her mother would say "Oh Betty, you've knocked the table over again, I suppose it's because you're so big".

Her younger brother picked up on this and started teasing her and calling her Big Bad Betty, later shortened to Bee-Bee. In spite of the abbreviation, Betty knew what her nick-name stood for. She was very fond of her brother and in time her size, her nick-name and her brother's affection for her were so intermingled that every time she lost weight she feared he would stop calling her Bee-Bee and that the two of them would lose their affectionate relationship. As a result she had unconsciously sabotaged every diet she tried as soon as she lost a few kilograms.

While overweight people may recognise they are overweight, their mental picture of themselves may be far from accurate. Many overweight people, when asked to view photos of other people and pick out one who is about as fat as themselves, will pick the picture of someone either much fatter or someone much thinner. Few of us have an accurate picture of ourselves as others see us.

Elizabeth had two older brothers who were fond of her and allowed her to share in some of their activities. The eldest, in his late teens when she turned eight, bought a sports car which could seat two people comfortably. From time to time she was allowed to squash in as a second person on the passenger seat. Invariably there were comments about it being lucky that she was so thin and that she'd soon be too big to go for rides with them. They nick-named her Skinny-Liz.

She dreaded putting on weight as she feared she might be excluded from the car rides. As she grew older and the car rides became less important, she feared unconsciously that if she was no longer thin she couldn't be called Skinny-Liz and would be forgotten by her brothers as they pursued their own lives. Associating herself with the name Skinny-Liz meant she had a real identity crisis whenever she put on weight.

Annabelle knew she was fat. She thought of herself as fat and often called herself a big fat slob. She did this particularly when sneaking biscuits from the biscuit tin, walking into a cake shop or embarking on a chocolate spree. She was overweight, but only by about 12 kilograms (2 stone), certainly not enough to be considered a big fat slob.

When you keep telling yourself you are a big fat slob your subconscious takes this in and reinforces it for you. You are fat, OK. What do fat people do? They eat, of course — so you eat. They overeat — so you overeat. Your behaviour lives up to your self-image. Annabelle had been doing this for years and was gradually getting heavier.

She was taught to think of herself as a slim person, temporarily in a body that was too big. With this in mind she was able to keep saying to herself "I really am a slim person". She created a mental picture of the thin Annabelle, hiding inside the fat body, rather like an actor in an over-sized outfit.

When she had gone shopping the highlight of the occasion had been when she found the best looking cake shop and went inside for the biggest cake and a hot chocolate. After our sessions she learnt to go round the shops saying to herself "I'm slim and attractive and would enjoy a crisp green apple". When the shopping was complete she would then buy her apple and head for the car. She quickly lost the 12 kilograms (2 stone).

Thinking of yourself as even fatter than you actually are is a reflection of the poor self-image many overweight people have. While it is true that many people claim to be "not fat, just cuddly", few overweight people are really satisfied with their looks or the way they feel about themselves. This poor self-image may have even worse consequences. If it extends to thinking you can never succeed at anything, you probably won't even start dieting; being sure you will fail, you consider there is no point in trying. Perhaps you started this book just because it promised that no diet was involved.

Other people describe themselves in terms of their job. In response to the casual social question, "Who are you?", you hear people describing themselves as a research scientist (implication: a serious-minded person, one who thinks that to pay attention to their body would be vain and frivolous) or as "just" a housewife with two children (implication: to spend money on myself and my looks would be to deprive the children). Conversely a thin woman, a single mother with limited financial resources discovered that being slim meant she was showing the world that she was loving and caring for her children because she gave them more food than she gave herself. There are businessmen who feel their girth is a reflection of their success. We may think we have come a long way from the Polynesian concepts of body size and wealth, but have we?

Brian fell into this category. He had always been slim. He came from a low-income family and had struggled to put himself through school by working at night. After a few years of working for other people he decided to start his own business. This meant long hours of work and pouring all the available income back into the business. During that time he went short of food and sleep and became even slimmer. Then the business started to pick up; he could employ more staff and hurried business meetings became relaxed business lunches. His colleagues made comments like "Come on, eat up, you look as if you can't afford to give yourself a square meal" and "If you're going to be prosperous you must look prosperous". Inevitably his frame filled out, his new lifestyle encouraged it, his subconscious sanctioned it.

He got a rude surprise when his doctor told him that, for the sake of his health, he would have to start losing some of the weight his successful lifestyle had encouraged. He agreed to go on a diet and all went well at first. He lost 6.5 kilograms (1 stone), and then became stuck. Not one to fail once he had set his mind to it, he came to see me. He discovered that the failure was due to his association that being slim meant being poor and over-worked. He was then able to get back on his diet and lose the next 12.5 kilograms (2 stone).

Your description of yourself may also include sexual and emotional associations. Some of these ideas may also be incorporated into your choice of weight.

Georgina thought that all slim women were flirts, in fact, "fast and loose tarts" was her silent appellation. She had been slim when she married but soon put on 6.5 kilograms (1 stone). She said it made her feel safe. It was her way of proclaiming to the world her fidelity to her husband.

As if to prove Georgina wrong, Alice was slim and not really interested in sex. She believed that being slim was a way of not being sensual and avoiding advances from men.

So you can see from this that there are people who think that being slim is protective and others who think being fat is protective. Neither is protective. To link your weight to the way you handle situations and to what you expect people to think of you is something that comes out of your past history but has little present validity. The sooner you can unhook these connections, the sooner you can take control of your weight.

Susan had no problem with food, she could eat sensibly and cut back when necessary, her downfall was drink. It wasn't that she was a heavy drinker, she never got drunk, she didn't have to have a drink. During the week if she stayed in her office at lunch time she would drink very little but if she went out to a business lunch, she would want wine. She enjoyed wine with her meals and liked to drink champagne on weekends. However much she cut back on her food intake, she got so many calories from the wine and champagne that losing weight was impossible.

She was asked to run the phrase "Something alcohol means to me is . . . " (For more information on Running a Phrase, please see the Tools section on page 77.) When Susan did this all we got was such things as: "drunkenness, debauchery, being out-of-control, disgracefulness, unnecessary, embarrassment, stupidity". Clearly, this was not getting a useful result.

She was then told to run the phrases "Something wine means to me is . . . " and "Something champagne means to me is . . . ". This produced much more useful results. She came up with the following completions: "pleasure, relaxation, sophistication, happiness, elegance, graciousness, style, having earned the time to relax and enjoy myself". Here was the answer to her problem. If having a drink or two in the evening or on weekends endorsed in her own mind that she was a sophisticated and successful woman who deserved luxury and pampering, then giving it up was going to be difficult.

Susan was encouraged to find other ways to get the same result so far as her self-image was concerned. One of her solutions was to drink mineral water from a wine glass at mealtimes, especially at lunch time. The use of an elegant stemmed glass, accomplished much of her goals and made her feel graceful in a way drinking from a tumbler never could. Sensibly, she did not deprive herself of wine altogether. But even when she had wine she had a second similar glass containing mineral water. She preferred not to dress this up with ice or a slice of lemon, preferring it to look as much like wine as possible. By working on other ways of creating the appealing image she got from drinking wine and by simply cutting down on the wine intake itself, she was soon able to lose weight.

Take some time now to make more lists of things you think are descriptive of you. In your first list put all the names and terms you use to describe your body, then list what other people say or have ever said about your body. Go back in your mind to your childhood and search out whatever was said about you in the past. Move slowly up to the present, recollecting everything anyone ever said about you that related to your weight or your size, and anything you thought about yourself in this context.

Analyse these lists. Firstly, let's take the list at face value. Tick off the things that were true and cross off the things that were not. The next step is to reassess the lists, checking the value of each statement. Ask yourself if it is helping you in your quest for your ideal weight. Roger did this and here is part of his list.

- "You're mother's big boy". (Not true — he only gained weight in his teens.)

- "Don't be such a big baby". (Not true — he wasn't big and, when this was said, he wasn't a baby.)

- "You're grown up now, big enough to look after yourself." (True but unhelpful to achieving his ideal weight.)

Now, reshape this list to describe yourself as you would like to be. Roger's list took the following form:

- I'm slim and good looking.
- I can easily touch my toes.
- My waist is 82 centimetres.
- I look good in my clothes.
- I look good in bathing trunks.
- I can run upstairs without puffing.

Once you have redefined your appearance as you wish it to be, commit the description to memory. Focus on this description at all times, particularly when you are eating or are around food but also as you go through your day in general. If, at this point, you are about to protest that this is all a lie, that this description does not fit the way you are now, even if it is the way you want to be — stop. Remember, this slim trim you does exist; it lurks there inside the fat and flab which you are trying to lose.

Now do a similar thing with your job or occupation. Do this by running the following type of phrase, "Being a housewife means . . . ", "Being a businessman means . . . " "Being an athlete means . . . ". Run it until you have as many associations as possible. Then assess the list in terms of the effect these ideas could have on your looks and your eating pattern. If you think being a housewife means being plump and homely, you are going to have trouble losing weight. If you think being an athlete means you must be slimmer than slim you will have trouble gaining weight.

In response to the instruction to describe themselves, a workshop participant wrote "I am a lonely, unhappy person who gets irritable easily, loves reading and painting and am currently living in a body that is too big for me". She had made the first step. Now it is your turn.

Describe yourself totally in terms of the you that hides in but is independent of your body and independent of your perceived role or occupation in life. Next, create this concept of yourself firmly in your mind and begin to build for it a body of the shape that you would like to have. Give this being the physical looks you would like. You will find that the person and the looks can come together *if you will let them* and, as we proceed through this book, you will find more and more ways of achieving this happy outcome.

MIND POWER

Few people recognise the power of the mind. For most of us, from a mental and emotional point of view, each day is like getting into a power boat with the engine running but with the rudder loose, waiting to see where it takes you. You may wake up wondering what sort of day it will turn out to be instead of making an active decision about the kind of day you want. From there, you let it take you where it will.

Veronica's days were like that. When she first came into the clinic she told me that she had once been a happy and contented person but had come to realise there was nothing exciting in her life and there was not likely to be any change. Her marriage had grown dull, the children had left home and there seemed to be nothing to look forward to. Her way of handling this depressing situation was to eat. She would plan her breakfast, her lunch, her tea and cakes and dinner. After each meal, if she still felt depressed, she would create a snack. In no time at all her weight had sky-rocketed. She had been on many diets but all had failed because they made her even more depressed.

Once Veronica realised the power of her mind she was able to change her mood. First, she was instructed to use affirmations the moment she woke. Even if the depression was lurking, she was to say, "This is going to be a wonderful day, I'm happy, excited and looking forward to it". Every time she found a negative or depressing thought forming she was told to create an alternative positive thought. The moment she was about to think, "Oh dear, I'm so bored" she was to think instead "Isn't life fun, there's this great book/film/walk I'm longing to read/see/do". After a while even her subconscious mind came to believe it and things began to improve.

Try it out for yourself. Next time you wake up thinking it's going to be a dreadful day, go along with it. Look for all the bad things that happen. Concentrate on all your woes. Complain to everyone who will listen and cry on all available shoulders. You'll soon find it is indeed a horrible day and that scores of dreadful things have happened. The lights were red, you got jumped in the queue at the post office, you snagged your clothing, someone cancelled a date, and so on. If you do it thoroughly, people may start avoiding you and then you can really feel deprived and depressed. To complete the experiment, use a day when you wake up happy. Tell yourself this is going to be a great day, concentrate on all the good things that happen, the green lights, the smiles you get, the compliments, the times people help you, the number of interesting phone calls you get. Comment on as many good things as you can to other people. Find out how many people you can make smile because you're happy. If you do this well, who knows what might result.

There are two aspects. Firstly there is what you choose to see or not see, hear or not hear, feel or not feel. Then there are the things that you actually change as a result of your mood. The first is called filtering. Your mind filters in the situations that agree with your expectations and filters out the situations that don't conform to them. Which would you rather do, filter out the good or filter out the bad? Wouldn't you rather choose to filter out the disagreeable ones? Then, choose, when you wake up, that this is going to be one of the good days. It really is as simple as that if you want it to be.

The second part of this scenario relates to what you can actually change by your own attitude. If you make a conscious decision to smile at everyone you meet (except where it might be misconstrued) you can be sure you will get a favourable response. If you choose to talk only about happy and positive things then the people you meet are likely to respond in kind. If you decide to frown and snap, the response will be different and you might even invite some arguments. If you talk about all the bad things that have happened and all the awful and boring things you have to do, people will almost certainly start to avoid you and you can be left with loneliness.

This part of the scenario is creative. By your own mood and actions you have actually contributed to a day that fulfilled your expectations, be they happy or sad, good or bad.

So there is both filtering and creating. Which type of day will you choose to create for yourself tomorrow? No-one can change your mind or your life but you. The ideas here so far are pragmatic, down-to-earth examples of the way your thoughts can influence your life. To try it out for yourself you don't even have to believe it, you just have to *do* it. If you do it with sufficient conviction, you will find that it works. It is easy to assume that thoughts just come and go as if they had a mind of their own, that we tend to forget who's boss. You can indeed control your thoughts. A further step is to recognise that your body obeys your mind and your thoughts.

This gets us back to where we started when I said you *are* the weight you want to be. You have thought your thoughts, programmed your emotions and so created a response in your eating pattern and hence the shape of your body.

Having recognised the input you have had into being your present shape, do not feel guilty about it. You had found the safest way to deal with all the situations from your past. If it was safer to eat and be fat, or not eat and be thin, than it was to deal with the emotional issues involved, then it made good sense for you to choose the safe way. Well done! The point now is, do you continue dealing with these issues in the same way? If you do, if you feel it is too scary to face up to the issues involved, then don't even try to change your weight. You are only setting yourself up for failure.

Worse than that, if you are overweight, every time you lose a bit and gain it back again, you will be making it harder to lose weight next time when you feel like facing the issues involved. This is because this yo-yo weight pattern creates less muscle weight and more fat. The less muscle you have in which to burn up the fat, the harder it gets to lose the weight. If, on the other hand, you want to deal with the issues involved, then do so. Forget about dieting for the moment. Concentrate on dealing with your history and the emotional triggers you have associated with eating. Deal with the relationships you have with people, your work, your possessions. Deal with your self-image and practise feeling good about yourself.

Weigh yourself before you start and record the weight, even though, initially, you will not be actively trying to lose or gain weight. You may be surprised to find how much weight the overweight can lose just by "mental dieting", or the Skinnies gain without consciously trying by learning to understand and by changing mental and emotional patterns. Once you have started on this course of action, you can choose almost any weight-loss or weight-gain plan and stick with it. For your health's sake choose a good one, one that gives your body all the nutrients it needs. The fine details are less important than what is going on in your mind and among your emotions.

PART TWO:
THE PAST

FOOD PATTERNS FROM THE PAST

It's now time to look into your personal history and we start this historical tour by focusing on food and what it has meant through the years.

To our primitive ancestors, living a hand-to-mouth existence in pre-historic days, eating was a fairly simple business. They caught or picked what they could when they were hungry. They ate according to their appetite and the availability of food. There were few, if any, mealtime rituals. They ate when they wanted to, not when the rest of the family or social group decided it. Eating had little if anything to do with pampering themselves, denying themselves or special social occasions. Yet, even in primitive times, when food was scarce, the amount they got to eat said something about their position in the pecking order. The stronger they were, the less likely they were to go hungry.

Today, by contrast, we have instilled many rules, associations and emotions around the process of eating so that the food itself sometimes seems to be secondary. Think of the upper classes in nineteenth-century England where even the topics for discussion at a dinner party were laid down. How much they ate and how much they left on their plate was indicative of their financial and social position. Think of the rituals surrounding meals in the Orient, tea ceremonies in Japan and feasts in Polynesia. In being less formalised and less conscious, our meals nevertheless have a powerful effect on our lives.

From the moment you are born, food is associated with love and belonging. After birth are you given love and hugs for their own sake or are they intimately connected with food from the start? If you are lucky, you are put straight onto your mother's breast. This is wonderful for bonding and reassurance. You heard that heartbeat when you were inside the womb and now, you can hear it through the chest wall. It sounds slightly different but is still the same heart-beat, and it presumably means that the same care and concern you received when you were inside the womb will continue to come from the same person, in this new phase of your life. This bonding process means that one of your very first associations is between being loved and being fed. The more you are loved the more you are fed and vice versa.

This is particularly true in your earliest experience of being nourished. Let's pursue this idea a little further. When did you get the most hugs, love and attention? When you were hungry? You started out feeling hungry and your stomach was empty. You were lifted on to the breast, the nipple was put in your mouth and the milk started flowing. At the same time your whole body was involved as you were hugged and massaged, you could smell your mother's familiar scent and hear sounds of endearment. All in all, the world was a pretty good place to be at that moment. Food was definitely associated with other good things, such as being wanted and cared for.

Then what happened? Gradually you got your fill, you could drink no more and you lost interest in the nipple. For one thing, you'd had plenty to drink, for another you were also full of air. You were then put over Mum's shoulder and hugged and stroked further as she tried to get you to burp. This leads to more associations between being full and being hugged and loved.

Knowing nothing of these technical details you burped and immediately felt less full and were then put down. The message is clear: feeling hungry means you are about to be fed and loved. Eating means being loved. The more you are picked up and fed, the more love you get. You are loved and stroked until you are full and put down (abandoned) when you have been burped. The way to get picked up and loved more is to show a determined interest in more nourishment. All is well if you are also loved and hugged when you are not hungry. If that happens the association may not be so strong and may not develop at all but many children are not so lucky.

What do you think your early feeding experiences were like? Maybe you were an only child and mother was able to give you her full attention. Maybe mother was back at work and had less time for you. Maybe there were other children around competing for attention and the one time you could be sure of your share was when she was feeding you. What was your mother's attitude to breastfeeding? Did she enjoy it or did she not like it? If she enjoyed feeding you, then you could grow up to associate food and love. If she did not enjoy it, you may have felt a confused tension between eating and being emotionally uncomfortable. The actual conclusions you drew from your own particular experience were yours alone. Another baby, in the same situation, may have drawn a different conclusion. Personalities are formed early. Take time now to think more about your early experiences, as you can recall them and as you can imagine them to have been, based on what you know of the people involved and their attitudes.

As a child it is easy to think that your parents know everything and are in control. Yet it may well be that your mother was very unsure of herself at the time. She certainly had all her own personal emotions and problems to deal with then, just as you have now. As a baby you were extraordinarily self-centred. You probably assumed anything that happened in your world was a direct reflection on you and your self-worth. Thus, some early conclusions about the role of food in your life, its importance and its meaning, and its relation to whether you were loved or unloved were formed. Recognising that your early experiences of food and of being breastfed were an important factor in generating your present relationship to food, set out to learn more. Discover as much as you can about your earliest meals, from your mother if she is still alive and if she will tell you. Alternatively, you can go back in your own memory to find this information.

Many mothers' response to a crying baby is to pick it up and stick something in its mouth. This may be the nipple, a bottle or a dummy. If, as a baby, you learnt that every time you were unhappy, lonely or frightened you would yell and would then be picked up and fed, it would have seemed to you that the way to deal with negative emotions was to eat. Is this what you are doing now as an adult? Are you eating as a solution to uncomfortable emotions? It never is a solution but it is hard to learn this when your early programming decided otherwise.

Come forward a year or two now and think back to the earliest formal meals you can remember. What were they like? What happened around the table. Did you get enough to eat? Were you persuaded to eat more than you wanted? Were mealtimes for the family harmonious or were they times of tension?

For Genevieve they were definitely times of tension. As a child, she was rebellious and naughty. She knew punishments would be handed down during the evening meal. So she learned to say she wasn't hungry, to avoid the meal and go to bed early, thus avoiding the tension and possible reprimands for the misdeeds of the day. She still has trouble eating dinner and often misses this meal with disastrous results on her weight. Since she only has time for a light breakfast and lunch she has trouble maintaining her weight.

Boarding schools are notorious for giving second helpings to those who eat the fastest, but boarding schools are not the only places where this occurs. In a large family you may have had to compete with your brothers and sisters for the best bits or second helpings. If you were an only child you may have had to eat fast to keep up with your parents. You may have learnt that Dad came first especially for second helpings. Since Dad was probably the biggest person in your world you may have concluded that when you grew to be big like Dad you could have first choice at food or even at other things, too.

There are many other associations with mealtimes. Were you told not to start until everyone was ready? Were you told not to speak and eat at the same time, not to speak with your mouth full? Were you told not to stretch, not to grab, to wait until things were passed to you?

Mary-Anne grew up in the house of her autocratic grand-mother being told that little children should be seen and not heard. Not fully understanding that the scraping of her knife and fork on the plate did not constitute noise, she spent each mealtime terrified that the smallest noise she made would result in her being sent out of the room. As a result she ate slowly and quietly and was always hungry when it was time to clear away. Later, she would ask her grandmother for snacks between meals. She learnt a pattern of eating that involved meals plus snacks, even when, as in later years, she ceased to fear the noise she made with her cutlery and ate a large meal. No wonder she became over-weight.

Not only are rules associated with mealtimes, other events may also take place round the meal table. Often the meals are the only times a family gets together. So they become the times when not only pleasant things are dis-cussed but grievances are also aired. Again, eating in the future may be fraught with this emotional association.

Take some time now to think back to your early meal experiences. Take your mind back to your earliest child-hood meals. Consider them slowly. Where did they take place? Was the table carefully laid or was the setting casual? Was there plenty of time or were meals rushed? Were they happy or tense times? What were some of the rules associ-ated with meals? Did you get the food you wanted or did you have to eat what you were given? How have all these things affected your current eating pattern?

Here is where the doing becomes important. Stop and get a pen and paper. Write down a description of your earliest meal. Then consider each year of your life and make notes on what the meals were like. Consider meals at home, at school, with friends, in restaurants. Who prepared the meals, did you have to help or were they provided for you? If you can't remember them, imagine what they would have been like, given what you know of the people involved and the circumstances at the time.

Having worked through your childhood meals, consider

meals as a young adult. What were they like, how did they reflect the meals of your childhood? What are your meals like now? How does this reflect the way they were when you were a child or a young adult? What patterns still adhere and are they still appropriate? Are they in your best interests in your quest for the slim and trim new you?

When you have written down all you can remember of the meals from your past, sit back and relax. Close your eyes and reflect quietly. Ask yourself again how your early experiences have affected your present attitude to food and eating. Ask yourself if these attitudes are helping you or if they are part of the reason for your being the weight you are now rather than the weight you (think you) want to be. Do this now or the information and the impact will be lost.

TREATS AND REWARDS

Now, it is time to consider what else you associate with mealtimes, with food and with eating.

Let's start with birthdays. On your birthday, as a child, you were special. It was the one day when you came first. What was the focal point? Of course there were the presents but there was also the party and the food. There were the cakes, the sweets, the biscuits, the ice creams and all the other treats. The food was the high point.

Then there was the special outing — a day in the country. Somehow it always seemed to centre around the picnic, the hamper and the esky. The high point was eating the picnic food, the anti-climax came when you had finished eating. Happiness was the anticipation, the searching for the right spot, the thinking about the coming meal and in eating and feeling full.

As adults we tend to carry on this theme. "Where shall we go for the day?" is often associated with "Where could we stop for a good lunch?" Again the meal is the focus of the day.

Christmas is a day that has seriously lost focus, particularly in cold climates where it centres around food. Who has not had their fill of turkey and all the trimmings followed by pudding and mince pies and then retired to the living room and gone on picking at glace fruits and sweets, even though eyes are also glazed and stomachs bloated, just to keep in touch with the convivial spirit of the day?

Going to the cinema is almost impossible without popcorn, ice creams and chocolates. Even if you are not hungry, you simply have to have them because it is part of the ritual. Adults are a little more sophisticated, although this may only mean that they make slightly less noise but some still insist that toffees with the names of film stars on the wrapping are an essential part of the outing. If you were programmed as a child to eat at the theatre you will probably eat or drink at the interval as an adult. I have even seen people queuing at the opera or theatre for a second drink while the warning bell was sounding and gulping it down on the run as they raced for their seats.

Clearly, we have come a long way from the days when food and eating was the means of satisfying a purely physiological hunger. Now, in our so-called civilised times, food and meals are associated with many rules and rituals, with many emotional needs and with much past history. They have become entangled with so many historical ties that it is no wonder we eat when we are not hungry, to fill emotional needs, because of ritual and habit, and that we overeat and gain weight for all sorts of unrecognised and subtle reasons. All of these rituals and patterns from the past do little for our health and can seriously hinder any attempts to lose or gain weight.

How about some other ritual meals? Was it the norm in your family to have a small supper before going to bed? If so, you may now, as an adult, feel you have to eat something at bedtime, even if you have just had a big dinner and are not hungry. Was it the norm to sit down to morning and afternoon tea? If so, do you still feel you have to do this, and do it, even if you are not hungry?

What a lot of things we associate with mealtimes and

eating. It may be helpful to you to run some phrases on this so that you can achieve a better understanding of some of your own associations. Use phrases such as: "Something meals mean to me is . . . ", "Something food means to me is . . . ". You could also run phrases associated with individual meals like "Something breakfast/lunch/dinner/supper means to me is . . . "

Learn all you possibly can about your relationship to meals, mealtimes, food and eating. Do the exercises again and even make up some of your own. Take time to dwell on all the meals you can remember in all the different settings in which you have eaten them and with all the people with whom you ate. That ought to keep you so busy you won't have time to eat.

CHILDHOOD MESSAGES

We will leave mealtimes now and look for other associations between food and aspects of your Self, your emotions and your life. What were some of the early messages you received about food?

It's interesting to wonder about the evolution of a child's sense of taste. As a baby you came into the world with no taste anticipation because your food source till then had by-passed your mouth. Your first taste sensation was breast milk and then whatever your mother gave you, vegetables, fruit purées or, heaven forbid, tinned baby food. It is sad to see mothers tasting the food they are about to give their child and then adding salt or sugar to make it more appealing. Until you are given salt and sugar, you do not expect them. Mother is already perverting your taste buds that are later violated by processed junk food. Many very young children enjoy vegetables. If they were spared the television ads, the food swaps of their peers and sugared presents from well-meaning friends and relatives, they might go on enjoying their vegetables. I advise mothers to give their children no sugar, no salt, no vegemite and no peanut butter. If they stick to this, it is amazing how long the child will continue to enjoy vegetables.

Thomas was an only child. For as long as he could remember both his parents had gone out to work. This meant that he'd had many different baby-sitters, both after school and in the evenings when his parents frequently entertained or went out socially. He was never happy about this and, although he could handle being cared for by a baby-sitter after school, he always cried when his parents went out in the evenings. The screams and tears as they left were usually more than the baby-sitter could stand so they would do all they could to distract him. In time, Thomas's parents learnt that lollies and chocolates were a way to keep him quiet until after they had gone. The baby-sitter was only too happy to keep up the practice until he went to sleep.

For Thomas the message was clear. Anytime he lost anything that was precious, or he couldn't have what he wanted, he would turn to sweets and chocolates for comfort. Once he realized where this pattern came from he was able to unhook the connection. He set about finding other ways to compensate for loss, other ways of getting satisfactory outcomes to situations. You can do the same thing, too.

Most children grow up thinking of food, and particularly sweets, as a reward. "Be quiet while we are shopping and you can have an ice cream on the way home" is a phrase you often hear in supermarkets. "Be good and I'll give you a sweet" is another. You were probably rewarded early on with sweets, rewarded for keeping quiet, rewarded for eating your vegetables (the implications for your weight in that are horrifying), rewarded for not touching things while out shopping, rewarded for not screaming while mother was talking to her friends. One way and another, you got the message. In this world into which you had come, sweet things were part of the good life.

There were messages that said to eat was good, that if you ate all your food you were a good child. If you picked at it, played with it and left it on your plate, you were a bad child. This, too, takes eating out of its role of providing bodily nourishment when, and only when, it is needed. It now has moral connotations of good and bad as well. For many parents, giving a child food is tied up with giving a child love. Similarly, a chubby child is a well loved child and a thin child is an unloved child. Who wants to tell the world they neglect or don't love their child?

From the child's point of view, rejecting food can be a silent way of rejecting the parent or of rejecting parental control and of being independent. Eating food is also accepting love. If you reject the meal your mother gave you, did she feel you were rejecting her love too? Many mothers feel this way if they dig deep and are honest enough to admit it. How else, the argument goes, can they show that they love you other than by nourishing and caring for you? So again you experienced pressure to eat. Perhaps you were made to eat everything on your plate, even if you were filled to the gills with food. This can certainly lead to an overeating pattern as a lifetime habit. Were you told, "Eat up and you'll grow big and strong", implying you would be weak and helpless if you didn't eat? Perhaps you were told that if you didn't eat your vegetables, you'd get no puddings or sweets, implying that if you ate a good meal you would then be rewarded by sweet foods, thus emphasising their desirability.

Perhaps you were a younger child and always wore second-hand clothes inherited from an older sibling. Mary was in that situation. All her clothes came from her sister Robin. Mary got fed up when she overheard her mother saying it was lucky that she was slimmer than Robin so that Robin's outgrown clothes fitted her. She resolved to get bigger the only way she could — sideways so that she would have new clothes bought for her in future. Her plan worked but she got fat and stayed fat. Once she realised why she was afraid to lose weight, that the old reason no longer applied and that she could buy new clothes when she became slim, losing weight was easy.

Beware how you programme your subconscious and be

warned that it has little sense of humour. If you say to yourself "If I eat any more I'll look like a pig", your subconscious may believe you and endeavour to do as it thinks you want and create the look of a pig every time you eat more. "I'll die if they offer any more cheesecake", may get you into real trouble. "Watch it, you'll get fat" could be taken by your subconscious to mean that simply looking at food will cause you to gain weight. Some people say, "I only have to look at food to gain weight". Remember how powerful your thoughts are. It would seem wise to eradicate such thoughts from your internal vocabulary.

Start instead to reprogramme your subconscious. Start affirming that fruit and vegetables are good for you, that you enjoy them and that you like simple foods without fat and sugar. Learn from your past and use this information to reprogramme your future.

THE SWEET TOOTH

In previous millennia, when the nearest thing to a candy store was a wild swarm of bees, the honey became the reward for the bee stings. It was useful then to have a sweet tooth. It sent you up trees after vitamin-laden fruits and it kept you away from the more bitter plants, many of them poisonous. Now, it is a serious metabolic and emotional detriment. You don't need a sweet tooth. Sufficient B group vitamins and some of the trace elements will see to it that sugar becomes much less appealing. (More in a later section on Supplements, see page 160.)

As a child I was encouraged to eat sweets. The argument seems to have been that if I had eaten enough sweets I would not need dinner. As a young adult I was disinterested in breakfast. Lunch was a sandwich followed by a bar of chocolate-coated toffee. Dinner was followed by a bag of toffees. Restaurants were not my favourite place as they never served toffees and entrees were uninteresting, I looked for a main course with fruit and dessert was the highlight. Fortunately, the dangers of sugar were impressed on me. I consumed quantities of Brewers yeast and B vitamins, cut my sweet intake by half, then into quarters and finally gave up. Now I wouldn't give you the time of day for sweets.

Yet, for most people there is still the craving and emotional involvement and again, it is the past catching up with them. All those boxes of chocolates on your first date, as reconciliation presents, as get-well-because-we-care gifts, speak of only one thing. Sugar shows you care and love. If you care about yourself, and of course you do, you came to feel that you must give yourself sweets as treats and that you must eat sweet things when you want to console or reward yourself or pamper and comfort yourself. It's all nonsense of course but deadly nonsense. Think about the words we use "Aren't you sweet", "It's sweet of you to help", "Whispering sweet nothings". Even Roget's Thesaurus adds to the meaning, equating sweet with such words as melodious, clean, agreeable and lovely.

So, it's no wonder that when you want to pamper yourself and show yourself that you care, you eat sweets. Sadly though, eating sweets only sets up the craving for more sweets, with disastrous effects on your weight. Afterwards you feel no happier than before, possibly less happy since you know what those sweets do to your waistline. Think back to all the times, particularly in your childhood, when you ate sweets or were given sweets. Make a list of all the things sweets mean to you.

Start with the phrase "Something sweets mean to me is . . . " and complete the sentence as many times as you can, listing the results. Remember not to filter what you write, no matter how silly it may seem when it first pops into your head. You will learn some very interesting things. Then, repeat the process replacing the words "sweets" with sugar, chocolate, cakes, biscuits, ice cream and so forth so that you run "Something sugar means to me is . . . ", "Something chocolate means to me is . . . ", "Something cakes mean to me is . . . ", "Something biscuits mean to me is . . . ", "Something ice cream means to me is . . . "

By now you should have quite a list. Sit quietly and mull it over. Look for the common denominator. You may be surprised at what meanings you actually attribute to sugar-laden foods.

PART THREE:
YOUR OWN SELF

YOUR INDIVIDUALITY

Wouldn't it be lovely to be accepted for yourself, exactly as you are, and to be allowed to do just what you want on the understanding that only you know what is best and right for you. No-one but you *can* know what is best for you. Do you feel that you know for sure what is best for some other person? Think about it. Do you know them so well that you have the ability and the authority to play God and decide how their life should be? If, for one minute, you think that the answer to this might be yes, turn the question around. Name one person to whom you would give total control over your life. Is there such a person? I would be surprised if there is. Yet much of the time people try, fruitlessly, to live up to another person's idea of what they should be. When this fails, it is all too easy to put on weight and hide behind it, or lose weight in an effort to disappear.

Toni felt she was expected to live up to other people's standards. She was the first child born to parents, particularly a father, who desperately wanted a son. Even her name told a story: Toni, Tony, Anthony, the name they would have given their son. The second, and last, child was also a girl. Toni felt she had had to live up to her father's expectations, yet, no matter what she did she felt she hadn't succeeded. She did well at school and went into the sciences and did physics instead of botany which she preferred, physics being the more masculine science. She went straight into a career and tried to share her work with her mathematician father. Yet, no matter what she did, she was still female. She felt she was supposed to be big and strong and to take over the role of the head of the house when her mother became sick and her father had a heart attack. Her defence was to get bigger in the only way she knew how — to gain weight. Once she understood why she was overweight it was easy for her to lose the unwanted kilograms.

In a study on the life of toddlers, a group of researchers

spent the day recording what was said to the children. It was found that the children received an average of nearly 450 messages to be different, such as, "Be quiet", "Stand still", "Stop making so much noise", "Speak up, answer me", "Don't bother me now", "Don't run in the street" and so forth. In contrast, they had less than forty messages that said they were OK as they were, things such as, "Well done", "That's good", "Mother's little helper" and "Thank you". Getting so little acknowledgment of their self-worth, it is no wonder these children grow up with identity problems.

We all know of families where the children are expected to take on the career of the parents, where the parents seem to live their lives through their children. There's the father who didn't go to university but is determined his children will. There's the family that runs a business and expects the children, or at least the oldest one, to take it over. There's the mother who married beneath her who is determined her daughters will marry into wealthy families.

These goals, set by parents, may play no part in the dreams and aspirations of the child. Yet, the child is made to feel that they should fulfil these dreams, that they should have desires similar to those of their parents, and if they don't, they are in some way inadequate.

Is it any wonder then that people grow up with a poor self-image and put on weight as an excuse for other failures? It is so much easier to be overweight and have this to blame for many perceived inadequacies than to face up to actually being found inadequate for oneself.

Did this happen to you? Run the phrase, "A way in which I was expected to be different as a child was . . . " and find out what you get. Is your weight now a rebellion against these expectations? Did you refuse to eat as a form of rejection of your parents' values or as a statement of your independence? Are you refusing to eat so that you can be different? Conversely, are you overeating as a compensation, as a different form of rebellion or to show you don't care?

None of these may apply. Find out for yourself what the truth is for you.

One of the easiest ways to become your desired weight is to decide to be yourself. Realise that no-one but you knows what is best for you. There is no "correct" way to live your life; there is only your way. Other people may like the person you become or may not like the person you become. Their opinion is a reflection of them, not of you. You cannot live a successful life if you are always trying to please other people because you can never be all things to all people and you are doomed to failure. Live your life by your own standards, be yourself and have the courage to do so. To be able to have the freedom to do this, and not live your life either conforming to what was expected of you or rebelling against it, you need to know yourself fully.

There are many ways to explore. They include rebirthing, a form of connected breathing in which old memories buried in your body and mind can surface and be dealt with. Clearing is a technique in which you are repeatedly talked back through past experiences so that you learn more about them and they lose their power. Using this technique, you can uncover things long forgotten. You can explore the different parts of your psychic make-up. There are physical techniques such as body harmony and mental ones such as guided meditation. You can do workshops, read books or consult counsellors. You can do any or all these things depending on how far you want to go. One thing is certain, by the time you have unravelled your true Self you will not have a weight problem.

YOUR GENES

A common cry of the overweight is, "It's all in my genes. It's not my fault. I have inherited the way I am and there's nothing to be done about it." They think that whatever they've got is what they're stuck with. This is a favourite excuse and that's all it is. While it is true that certain characteristics do lurk in your genes, it's not true for the overweight because there is no specific gene for being overweight. However, there is good evidence that at least half of the way you are is due, not to your genes, but to your environment and this is something you can work at understanding and then alter.

Elsie came to see me wanting to lose weight but said there was probably nothing she could do as it was in her genes and all her family were fat. Her mother and brother came with her on her next visit and I saw what she meant. Father, too, I was told, was overweight. It was a family trait and there was nothing to be done about it. Then I investigated their eating habits and found mammoth meals with one horrendous excess after another. Elsie's grandmother had always prepared meals this way and her mother, in turn, had grown up with it and considered it normal.

Elsie gave weight-loss a valiant try, by dieting only as she was not interested in the mind approach, but with little success. Three years later she was taller but much the same overall shape. At this stage she told me she had just left home, was cooking for herself, had little time, money or skill and wanted advice on what to eat. Her main health problem was her skin, her face was a mass of acne and a social embarrassment. Neither of us mentioned her weight but I mapped out a convenient eating pattern for her that would fit within her capabilities and help her skin.

She tried the new food regime and became convinced that it was good for her. We had not mentioned weight-loss so there was no threat or challenge in her mind nor was there any restriction as to quantity. All she wanted was to clear up her skin and this was enough to keep her to the programme. She was a lot more surprised than I when she returned a month later 3 kilograms (7 pounds) lighter. At this point she began to consider that maybe her weight wasn't in her genes and maybe she could do something about it. She could and did.

Just to show the cussedness of genes I will tell my own story. My aunt had a lovely figure until she went to live in the tropics, where weight dropped off her and she became a bag of skin and bones. In an age where curves were beautiful this was a problem. Only by going back to a cool climate could she regain her former figure. Shortly before I planned to go and live in the tropics myself, she said that, since we were so similar, the same thing was bound to happen to me. She insisted that I eat up and put on some weight. I did, and with her cooking it was easy to have second helpings. Then I went to the tropics and instead of losing weight, I immediately started to gain. This had never happened before, I had always been slim, no matter what I ate. Suddenly I was faced with having to consciously restrict my food intake (I knew little of the power of the mind then) and watch my measurements. I did manage to stop the increase but was unable to lose what I had gained until I returned to a cooler climate, at which point the weight fell away.

If you think you are limited by your genes, then you are. They certainly make a good excuse for doing nothing. But whatever your genes, you can always make the best of them. You may be big-boned but you don't have to be big-bummed. You may be short but you don't have to be circular.

Some people will gain weight to "get back at" someone, usually their parents. If this sounds silly, remember that they rarely do it consciously. Jennifer was a clear example of this pattern. Her mother had been very elegant and had brought Jennifer up to be well-mannered and dainty. Her clothes had to be neat and tidy and she had to behave correctly at all times. Her eating habits had to be elegant and she must keep a trim figure. After years of this programming, Jennifer felt so restricted she wanted to scream. She felt that, in the interests of behaving properly, she had been deprived of the fun she should have had as a child but she didn't dare to break the pattern until she married.

Her husband was much more relaxed and gradually Jennifer began to change. The thing that gave her most pleasure now was eating large meals. It was almost as if, at the end of two slices of her favourite cheese cake, she was thumbing her nose at her mother and all the restrictions she had imposed. If this seems a self destructive pattern, remember that it was not done consciously. Jennifer thought of herself much more as a child having a forbidden treat than an angry woman venting her anger at her mother.

Did your mother diet? Was she conscious of her figure and did you grow up hearing about calories and weight reducing programmes? If so, how has this affected you? Do you too feel that you must think in the same way or did you rebel and decide you would have none of it, that you would eat what you liked and to hell with it?

This whole issue of conforming or rebelling is interesting. So many people that come into the clinic are rebelling against their parents in their bid for freedom. Yet the mere fact of rebelling shows they are not free. You are not making your own free choice of what you will do or will be when you do either the same as or the opposite to your parents: they are still pulling the strings. To be free you have to choose your actions independently and as suits the individual you.

YOUR EMOTIONS

Ask almost any overweight person why they eat and they will often acknowledge that their emotions play a large role in shaping their eating patterns. Do you know *why* you eat when you're not hungry? Do you know *why* you crave chocolate fudge sundaes? Do you know *why* you get hungry at four o'clock every afternoon? Do you know *why* you feel compelled to go on eating after big special occasion meals? No, probably not, or you wouldn't be overweight and you wouldn't be reading this book. There are many emotional reasons for eating. Here are some of them and you can add to the list for yourself. You may overeat for any of the following reasons:

• You didn't get enough love as a child.

- It makes you feel good.
- You make up for other things you could be missing out on.
- No-one else pampers you enough so you must do it yourself.
- You're bored and there is nothing to look forward to in your day.
- You've worked hard and you deserve a treat.
- You don't want to do the next task so you delay it with a snack.
- You like the taste of food.
- Food is one of your chief pleasures.

You get fat because:

- It gives you a safe excuse for not having a boy or girl-friend.
- It saves you from advances from men.
- People will not expect so much of you.
- You can blame it for any other problems in your life.
- If you put yourself down, other people are less likely to.
- You don't want other people to envy you.
- It gives you a reason not to be as successful as other people.
- You get your own back at your mother.

Complete this sentence as many times as you can "A reason I eat is ... ", "Another reason I eat is ... " and continue prodding at your subconscious until you feel it has given you its all. Then sit down and go over the list. Look for other ways of achieving all those results, ways that don't involve eating.

Notice that some of your reasons are appropriate but most are not. Of course, it is fine to eat when you are hungry. It is also good to like the taste of what you eat and food will indeed make you feel good when you need it. But let's look at the other reasons.

Joan was a schoolteacher, a career she had somehow

fallen into when she hadn't known what else to do. She had enjoyed it initially but no longer did. All the marking of papers at home was tedious and marking the exam papers was the worst job of the lot.

When she got home in the middle of the afternoon, she was then faced with the marking and used the excuse of a cup of coffee and something to eat to delay the start. After she got started, she rewarded herself with food at intervals throughout the time she spent on the papers. The weekends were even worse. Because she was so bored with this part of her work, she did only a little at a time and then left her desk and roamed around the flat. As a result, the work took the whole weekend to do and the weekend became one long nibbling binge.

Her first step to weight-loss was to list all the other things she could do as permissible reasons for having a break. These included reading a chapter of her current book, playing music and phoning a friend. But her best solution was to take care of her body. She decided that every time she felt she must have a break, she would look after another bit of herself. So she did her nails, put on a face mask, washed her hair, plucked her eyebrows, lathered body cream all over herself or did specific exercises. By the time she was through, she was not only slimmer but very trim and well-groomed.

Her second step was to change her job. With her new interest in looks and skin care she did a beauty course and now helps other people to lose weight while she's giving them a facial.

Tessa's list related to the second part. She had "I got fat because . . . I ate too much, I like being cuddly, I like food, I wanted to be loved . . . " This last one set her thinking. What did it mean? Tessa was fifty when she came to see me. Her three children were all married and she had five grandchildren. She was often lonely and, more than anything, wanted to see more of the three families and her grandchildren. When we went back into her childhood Tessa recalled that her own grandmother had been fat and had been the person Tessa ran to whenever she wanted comfort. Her mother worked and had often been harassed and cross and had little time for hugs. Mother was slim and wore clothes that had to be kept smart and not rumpled by childish exuberance. Grandmother, on the other hand, had been large and cuddly, with plenty of time to have Tessa in her lap telling stories of her own young life. Her sub-conscious belief was that if she wanted the grandchildren to come and see her, she had to be fat and cuddly. What a clever and devious thing is the subconscious.

It can also happen the other way round. You may be choosing your present weight so that you can be as unlike someone as possible. Fred did just that. His much older brother John was a big man, tall, solidly built and prosper-ous, the pride of his father's heart. There was little love lost between the brothers. Fred saw John as a pompous hyp-ocrite and swore that when he grew up he would be entirely different. He was. But unfortunately this extended from personality to looks and, since John had been well built, if anything slightly on the heavy side, Fred chose, unconscious of what he was doing, to be thin. Once he recognised this, and that he would not become more like his brother if he increased his girth, it was much easier for him to gain the extra weight.

Helen's list produced a more unusual reason for being fat: " . . . because I will not be bought". This had popped out in a verbal session, when she was no longer monitoring what she said. It took her by surprise and she wanted to stop and explore it then and there.

When she was young, her mother, a single parent, had often had periods of illness when she could no longer cope with her two children. Helen and her brother Peter were then sent off to various relatives. One of their destinations was to the home of their grandmother. She was unemotional, not particularly demonstrative and not keen on having two noisy children around the house. However, she did care for them in her own way and also felt she should do her best for them. Her way of showing affection was to prepare tempting meals for them and then press them to have second helpings.

This, at least, was Helen's interpretation of the situation. As a result she refused to eat what her grandmother had prepared. She wouldn't, as she saw it, be bought. She would have the smallest helping possible and refuse a second, no matter how hungry she was. At the end of the meal she would leave the table, still hungry, and then look for any food she could find. Her pocket money went on sweets, she swapped toys with her friends for food, she ate more than she really wanted to cover up her loneliness and hurt.

This set her lifetime eating pattern. Neither her children nor her husband, could understand how she was so over-weight. They all knew how little she ate at mealtimes. It was only after an accident left her bed ridden for three months and deprived her of access to the kitchen, that she realised her formal meals, which were brought to her in bed, had formed only a small part of her daily food intake. In her case, she was lucky. She lost all her excess weight easily — in bed. Too embarrassed to tell the family that her usual meals were no longer enough and that she spent the time permanently hungry, she had come to me to sort the situation out, hoping she could find a way of avoiding a return to her former overweight state. She did, and has now trained herself to eat only at mealtimes and to be comfortable with letting the family see the amount she eats.

Again and again sex, or the avoidance of sex, comes up as a reason for being overweight. Melanie had no idea why she was overweight, she also had no idea why she felt so ner-vous when men asked her to go out on a date. She was, at thirty-seven, still single and had very few men friends. In her case the past was so locked away that it only came out after several regression sessions.

As a sixteen-year-old she had become pregnant to her first serious boyfriend. She was still at school, her parents had known nothing about it and her boyfriend had arranged for an abortion. After the operation he had taken her to a girlfriend's house, where she was to spend the weekend, but had then abandoned her. She had been ill and bleeding for several days, yet too terrified to tell her parents. All together the whole thing had been so traumatic she had buried it. Her defence, as she grew older, was to put on so much weight that no-one would want to make love to her again and there would be no further risk of pregnancy.

Like all the other situations, once she realised the reason for her actions she was able to start changing them. You need to be totally honest with yourself and be willing to expose the emotions behind your eating pattern.

- Are you the hostess with the mostest, yet so nervous you pick at all the food even before the party starts?
- Do you eat to calm your nerves, afraid of what the boss will say about your latest project?
- Are you shy at parties and stay in a corner eating?
- Do you eat for fulfilment, to fill in time, because you're bored or to pamper yourself?
- Do you eat for reassurance that you are in control or as rebellion, to show you can do what you like?
- Do you eat when you are lonely or feeling insecure?
- Did you feel deprived as a child and do you now eat just to show you can have whatever you want?

Check yourself as you do the exercise above. Do this, too. Every time you are about to eat, sit down first and write a list headed "The reason I am about to eat is . . . "

The emotional eater has a lot to contend with because food means much more to them than only nourishment. Yet, once you have identified the emotions that send you into the kitchen cupboards, you have taken the first step to finding other ways to deal with these emotions and handle these needs. After that, you can lower your weight.

YOUR REACTION TO STRESS

Stress is something we talk about, pay attention to and

blame for many things that go wrong. One wonders how something that doesn't exist has acquired such fame.

As an independent entity, stress doesn't exist because there is no such thing as a stress: there is only the way that you react to situations. The internal changes in you, as you respond to something external, are your manifestations of stress. Stress is measured by the response of your body or your mind to external stimuli.

Let's take a couple of examples. Charles enjoyed his work, especially the lecturing. He enjoyed talking to groups of people — giving a lecture, an after-dinner speech or a presentation in a boardroom. But a small dinner party where he had to make general and witty conversation overheard by his neighbours caused him total embarrassment.

For Tom, it was the other way around. He hated talking to large groups of people. The time he had to make a speech as best man at a wedding had been a nightmare. He was at his best in casual conversation, amusing the people around him.

Stress for Charles was small social chitchat and talking to a large audience was exhilarating. Stress for Tom was talking to a large group of people and casual social chatter was a relaxation and fun.

Perhaps even the word "stress" has become overused and distorted. At the ultimate level, everything we do is a stress. Getting up is a stress (it's easier to lie in bed), smiling is a stress, work is a stress, going away on holiday is a stress. The world would be an awfully dull place if no stressors were applied.

The point may be more clear if we use the term "challenge" instead of "stress". Everything you do and everything that happens to you is a challenge of some sort, small or large. The point is whether or not it falls within your comfort zone. The ones that fall within your comfort zone are part of your comfortable living pattern. The ones that fall outside your comfort zone cause distress and discomfort, physically as well as mentally. These are the ones you call stresses.

You can learn a lot from the challenges that fall outside your comfort zone as the perceived stresses in your life. If something upsets you, find out why. If something makes you angry, find out why. And while you are running phrases and trying to unravel the real meanings of these things, be aware of one thing: you are never upset for the reason you think.

Elizabeth thought Duncan was a terrific guy. The only thing that bothered her was that every time they went out to dinner he insisted on explaining each dish on the menu to her. When they got married this expanded. He instructed how each new appliance worked, how she should do her tax forms now she was married — he explained everything to her, even if she already understood it. Each time he started to do this she got angry.

She was told to run the phrase "The reason his explanations make me angry is ... " She came up with several trivial completions then we hit: " ... because it means he thinks I don't know" and " ... because it means he thinks I'm stupid". At this point her face lit up. She recalled as a child her older brother insisting on reading everything for her saying as he did so "I can read and you can't. You're stupid". Now every time Duncan read or explained something to her, she interpreted it as *him* thinking her stupid. Duncan's insistence on explaining reactivated her childhood pain of being called stupid. He, on the other hand, thought he was being kind and taking care of her.

Whenever Rowena had to visit the bank or the post office she tried to pick the fastest moving queue. If she guessed wrong, she became angry. Driving home she would try to pick the fastest traffic lane; if she chose the slow one, she became furious. If two lanes merged or another driver pushed in front of her, she became irate. Every time she was held up, she felt stressed and cross. She ran the phrase "The reason I get mad when someone pushes in front of me is ... " and the completion was " ... because it means I'm no good, I'm less important than the others".

Her mother had taught her good manners from an early

age and Rowena had grown up with the injunction to let other people go first. Other people helped themselves first, went through doors first, were served first in shops. Rowena was to stand back, offer her place to others, let other people be, do, have what they wanted ahead of her; this was all good manners. Yet Rowena had felt inadequate each time her mother pushed her to the back, convinced it meant that her mother thought she was less important than other people and that she loved her less. Now, each time she missed out in a queue she felt inadequate and belittled and became angry. When she understood the cause of her feelings of stress, and why she got angry, it was easy to relax. She chose to affirm, "I am letting them go ahead because I am more generous than they are", and this made her feel better and helped her deal with many situations in a more relaxed way. It was certainly better than gobbling down food as if it had caused the offence.

Make a list of all the things that stress you and then run the phrase "The reason . . . stresses me is", "Another reason . . . stresses me is . . . " until you have all the responses you can come up with. Find out what this says about you. Consider ways this could be hindering you in your aim to lose or gain weight.

It is not only who and what you react to that counts; it is the way you react. Do you bottle it up or let it out? If you were told as a child that it was unseemly to make a fuss, a sign of weakness to cry or cowardly to complain of pain, you probably deal now with stressful challenges by suppressing them. This cannot go on indefinitely and, needing some other form of outlet or solace, you may have turned to food.

The more you learn about yourself, the healthier and slimmer you can be. Use awareness of the things that stress you and your responses to them as a tool in achieving a better understanding of yourself.

YOUR SELF-IMAGE

We have seen that your self-image was shaped early in life. When you were born, the slate was clean. When people told you what a lovely cuddly bundle you were, what a big girl or boy you were becoming, or what a skinny little thing you were, how you were growing up just like so-and-so and what a pity it was that you didn't take after someone else, you had begun to get some sort of picture of who you were — at least in their eyes.

As the years went by, this picture was extended. Other children at school would have called you fatty or skinny, beanpole or shorty, in the inimical way of children. You would have heard about your appearance and its acceptability or non-acceptability, your capabilities and your weaknesses. Your teachers would have added to it with such remarks as, "Do stand up; no point in trying to hide your height" and comments on your girth in the gym.

Much of this is done with little thought for your self-image, yet it is shaped by these very remarks. The teachers, all too concerned with the perceived dangers of self-satisfaction and conceit, would have felt it their duty to point out your faults. Even affection and praise could be hidden behind humorous rebukes.

The trouble is that when you are very young you have no sense of humour. Think of the times when you, as an adult, have seen a toddler drinking in every word of a preposterous story being told to them by a joking adult, and you will see what I mean.

Jennifer, at six, was sent to boarding school. She gained considerable weight in her first term on school food. The doctor, when he saw her after an asthma attack, grabbed a fold of flesh at her waist, and said that it "would have to come off". Terrified that when he returned the following week, he would bring a knife and cut it off, she refused to eat for a week.

Such friendly phrases as "Come on you idiot", "Hurry up

stupid" or "Run faster, lazybones" can easily be taken seriously by a child not sure of his or her self-worth. Once this image is established, it can be hard to change. It may also be hard to recognise how far it is from the truth. If you were always told by the people you love that you had certain physical inadequacies you would surely come to believe them. Be aware that these people did not intend to harm you, they were fond of you, and much of what they said was meant as endearment. It is how you interpret it that counts.

Think of the people you know who have what you consider to be a false image of themselves. There is the beautiful woman who is convinced she is unattractive and forever focuses on the tiniest wrinkle on her face, the slim woman who's certain she's fat, the fat man who thinks he's "well-built" or the successful person who considers themselves inadequate, the popular person who believes she is only invited out socially because of her husband.

Perhaps your own self-image could be askew. Find out how others see you. The best way to do this in regard to your appearance might be to go to a beauty consultant, someone who doesn't know you and who has no axe to grind.

Your self-image is made of what is reflected back to you by the world at large, other people's comments, their expressions and their actions. It comes from mirrors and from things you overhear. It also comes from the way you interpret this reflection. Because of this last factor, you can change your self-image. You can choose to feel better about yourself than you do at this moment; you can focus on your good points and forget or change the rest.

Think of a time when you were dressed for a gala occasion and had a terrific time, confident that you looked your best and were being admired. When you got home you found there was a dirty mark on your back or part of your underclothes were showing or a zip was undone. So what? You thought you looked terrific and had a great time.

The opposite can also happen. You can go out convinced your hair is a mess, your clothes are all wrong or no-one wants to talk to you. The next day you learn that the other people thought you looked great but felt shy of approaching you as you seemed so aloof. You thought you looked dreadful and were shunned so you had an unhappy time.

Which of the two will you have? It's up to you. If you want to go for the happy outcome, start thinking positive thoughts. If you think negative thoughts, you'll get the unhappy outcome.

Here is an exercise to find out more about your self-image and the way you think of yourself. Answer each of the questions below as well as the follow-up questions. Give yourself plenty of time with each one and come up with as many answers as you can. Don't filter your responses, let some free association come into play and write down any ideas that pop into your mind, even if they seem silly or irrelevant. To some questions you may feel like answering both yes and no, so do it both ways, with two sets of follow-up answers to the last part.

- If you know a social event is coming up do you go on a diet? . . .
- Why? . . .
- What does that say about me? . . .

- Have you turned down a social invitation because you felt too fat or too thin? . . .
- Why? . . .
- What does that say about me? . . .

- Who in your family comments about your weight or your shape, even obliquely? . . .
- How does that affect me? . . .
- Why? . . .
- What does that say about me? . . .

- Could you be more effective if you were slimmer or less thin? . . .
- Why? . . .

- What does that say about me? . . .

- Have you ever lost a promotion or job because of your weight? . . .
- Why? . . .
- What does that say about me? . . .

- Do you think other people treat you differently because you are fat or skinny? . . .
- Why? . . .
- What does that say about me? . . .

- Would things be better if you were slimmer or less thin? . . .
- Why? . . .
- What does that say about me? . . .

Here are some of the results culled from the workshops:

In answer to "If you know a social event is approaching do you go on a diet?" came "Yes". It says I am ashamed of myself the way I am. I think I would be more popular if I was slimmer. I need a specific goal before I will do anything about my weight. Other people's opinions of me matter more than my own.

In answer to "Have you turned down an invitation because you felt too fat or thin?" came "Yes". It says I'm ashamed of my weight. People will only like me if I'm slim. I'm conceited. We also had "No". This means I don't care about my looks. My looks don't matter. People like me as I am so why should I bother to lose weight?

In answer to "Who in your family comments, even ·obliquely, on your weight?" came from a very thin man in his early twenties "Father". It upsets me. My father's opinion matters to me. He's a man so he should know. It means he doesn't approve of me. It means I'm not good enough. It means I'm a weakling (from a Skinny). From an overweight woman came "Mother". It pleases me. I'm fat like her and that makes me feel safe. I win. I'm showing her I can eat what I like now.

In answer to "Could you be more effective if you were slimmer or less thin?" came "Yes". My looks are more important than me. I think I'm only liked for my body. You can't be successful when you're fat. Yes I could be stronger if I wasn't so scrawny. And "No". My looks aren't important. I don't think my weight matters. I'm valued for my brains. This came from someone who thought they *ought* to lose weight but had no real desire to.

In answer to "Have you ever lost a job or a promotion because of your weight?" came "Yes". I blame my failures on my weight so they are not really my fault. You have to be big to be strong and important (from a Skinny).

In answer to "Do you think other people treat you differently because you are fat or thin?" came "Yes". I'm constantly aware of my weight. I blame my weight for my problems. No-one would like me for myself. I'm embarrassed by my weight.

In answer to "Would things be better if I were slimmer?" came "Yes". It must mean I like things to be bad. I'm stupid for staying fat. I think my weight is important. I'm afraid to have a good time.

Check over your own answers and find out what you can learn from them. When you start seeing yourself in a favourable light, others will do so, too.

YOUR DIET

I promised you no diets and no dieting programmes. This section is not one in which you will be told what to eat and what not to eat but one in which you will discover how you feel about diets.

Having come this far, you will already know something about the way you feel when diets and dieting are under discussion but there is more to explore. The subconscious mind is inventive and can come up with a million reasons why now is not the right time to start to lose weight. I once put an advertisement in the local paper asking for people who wanted to lose weight to enrol as part of a study in which I was going to compare three different approaches to weight loss. Many people answered the advertisement and the phone was almost constantly ringing. Everyone that phoned wanted to talk about their weight and about dieting. They all professed themselves keen to start, but as it got nearer and nearer the time to be committed, they came up with more and more reasons why the time was not right. I was told it would be more convenient after the school holidays; it would be more convenient during the next school holidays; it would be better for them to start in the winter; it would be better for them to start in the summer; there were important social occasions coming up. They were all willing to start any other time but not now.

Others would produce reasons why they couldn't go on a diet such as:
- I have to cook for the family.
- My husband/wife will feel nervous if I become more attractive.
- My husband/wife likes me the way I am.
- I have to eat out so much.
- Everything I eat turns to fat so I would spoil your study.
- Diets never work for me.
- I'd have to give up the foods I love.
- It's boring.
- There's no point as the weight comes back on again.
- You have to be hungry all the time.
- It's too difficult.
- It takes so long.
- I think I'll just eat less; I don't need a diet.

Before we go any further, it is time for you to do some work for yourself. Run the phrase "Diets are . . . " as many times as you can and find out what you get. Then run the phrases

"The way I feel about dieting is . . . " and "I can't lose weight because . . . ". having done this let's take a look at the first list, your completions to the phrase "Diets are . . . ". How many positive things did you find to say about diets? How many negative things? The chances are you found very few positive things and lots of negative things to say about diets. This has to change or you are setting up mental blocks right from the start.

Back to work. Before we go any further, make a list of all the positive thoughts you relate to diets. Ideally, you should develop a positive list that is longer than the negative list. If you feel this is impossible, think a bit more. Here are a few positive ideas to get on with.

Firstly, let's look at the dictionary and you will find something like "Diets are a way of feeding, a prescribed course of food". There is nothing here to say that they have to involve a restriction of foods. Weight-loss diets are only one type of diet. You can have diets to gain weight, to maintain weight, to cleanse the system. Diets can be good for your heart, make things easy for your kidneys and improve your sports ability and so forth. It's interesting that so many people immediately think of weight loss when the word diet is mentioned. Now, let's think about weight-loss diets specifically and consider some of the possible good comments you could make. They could include the fact that diets help you to be slim, make you healthier, enable you to like your body better, improve your skin, make you fitter and allow you to explore new foods as you change out of your present eating rut and experiment with new dishes. Now make your own list. You may have to think for a while but it is in your own best interest to make this as long a list as possible.

What about the second phrase, what completions did you get to the phrase "The way I feel about dieting is . . . "? How many of those completions are negative? These must all be changed around to something positive and then used as affirmations. Here are some examples of what is meant.

If you said "It means I have to go without", you could change it to "Dieting means I can eat lots of new salads" or

"Dieting means I can eat more refreshing foods, such as fruits". If you said " . . . boredom", you could change it to ". . . the opportunity to try new dishes". If you said " . . . not eating the foods I love" you could change it to " . . . learning to love new foods". By now you should be getting the hang of it. Convert all your negative ideas about dieting into affirmations.

Just a word of warning though — beware of reinforcing the negative. For instance changing "something dieting means to me is . . . boredom" into "something dieting means to me is . . . not being bored" doesn't work. The subconscious ultimately focuses on the last two words, " . . . being bored" because, like you and me, it is lazy and prefers to concentrate on what is familiar.

Now let's move on to the third phrase you ran, "I can't lose weight because . . . ". Before we start, when you have milked this phrase for all it's worth, put it on the banned list. This is not a useful phrase to have running around among your mental dross or among your affirmations. Now, to business.

I will work through the list I gave above since it is likely that many of these crop up in your list, too.

BECAUSE I HAVE TO COOK FOR THE FAMILY.

So what? Do you want to make them fat too? Will it hurt them to have more slimming foods for a while? It might help them to have healthier hearts and arteries and it might help them to lose weight, too. Equally, there is no reason why you have to eat as much as they do. Make a side salad, it's good for them all, then omit the spaghetti on your plate, have the meat sauce and a side salad with it. Share the quiche with them, eat the centre of your slice and give the pastry to the dog.

If you don't have a dog it might be a good idea to get one. While staying with friends recently I watched with interest while my host dispensed with the food he didn't want by giving it to his pet. He had been told that he had to lose weight, but he hadn't yet fully changed his habits. At breakfast, he was used to having three slices of toast. He now had only the first two slices. Then, because everyone else was still eating, he took the third slice and slowly fed it to the dog. By then we had all finished and were ready to clear away. At lunch and dinner he would eat part of his meal, then give the rest to the dog. At afternoon tea time he automatically picked up a biscuit, realised he shouldn't be eating it, and gave the rest to the dog. Fortunately the dog was a large and very slim stray recently saved from the pound and showed no signs of getting fat.

MY HUSBAND/WIFE WILL GET NERVOUS IF I BECOME MORE ATTRACTIVE.

If this is the case, it points to problems within the relationship that need attention. It is hardly an adequate reason for one of the partners to risk their health by overeating and being overweight.

Tony and Fiona were an example of this situation. Tony had been a very popular and happy bachelor when he met Fiona. He was tall, slim and good-looking with a reputation for sweeping women off their feet and he worked in the fashion industry where there was no shortage of attractive women. Fiona continued to work for a while after their marriage, then stopped, had two children and became involved in domestic pursuits.

All too aware of her husband's earlier reputation and continuing opportunities, she became suspicious and jealous and she fretted when he had to be away from home. Nothing was further from Tony's mind; he was happy with his marriage and his settled home after his previous nomadic bachelor existence. Unfortunately, nothing he did could turn Fiona from her view that, if not already unfaithful, he soon would be and the rows and tension grew.

Then Tony began to gain weight and was not so slim and attractive. Unconsciously, Fiona began to relax and fed him more and more food. Tony, also unconsciously, welcomed the food as a sign that Fiona still cared. He welcomed the weight, since he felt safer and even less inclined to stray, thus protecting the marriage that he valued. All this surfaced when we tried to work out why Tony was having trouble losing weight. As the underlying problem emerged, they were both able to look at it and work on it and themselves. Happily, Tony then lost weight and the marriage became even stronger.

MY HUSBAND/WIFE LIKES ME THE WAY I AM.

This is akin to the one above but without the tensions. Through the years Veronica had fretted over her weight gain. Some of the weight had crept on gradually and most of it remained after the birth of each of her three children. Derick, her husband, in an effort to please and reassure her, maintained that he loved her just the way she was, making a joke of the fact that there were no hard bones to jab him now when he hugged her, and insisting that overweight women were much more jolly and easier to get on with.

The fact was that he did miss the slim woman he had married, but he loved her and cared about her much too much to want to hurt her. He also liked her to be happy and at ease with him rather than fretting about her weight. Veronica had grown to believe this and it had sapped her determination to lose weight again and had even given her tacit approval to gain more weight. She knew she would feel better slimmer, but it always seemed too much trouble and, with Derick's seeming approval, she didn't bother.

I HAVE TO EAT OUT A LOT.

Many people find they eat several meals a week in restaurants as part of their social and business life but this is no reason to gain weight. Do not give up this social pattern. If, in your mind, trying to lose weight becomes associated with having to give up your social customs and the dining out that you enjoy, then losing weight will seem like a double deprivation and you may feel defeated before you start.

Some restaurants seem to specialise in rich and fattening foods. Other restaurants seem to specialise in simple, low-calorie foods. This means that the first step to combining your lifestyle with a slim body is to choose the restaurant wisely. If, every time you go to an Italian restaurant you find yourself tucking into a large plate of spaghetti with a rich sauce or a large pizza with all the trimmings, avoid Italian restaurants. If every time you go to a Chinese restaurant you eat sweet corn and chicken soup followed by sweet and sour pork in a rich batter and sauce, don't choose a Chinese restaurant.

If, on the other hand, you love the way the Italians cook fish and the Chinese stir fry their vegetables, then monitor your menu choices. Remember, you go to a restaurant for many reasons. You go for the company, either business or social, for convenience so you don't have to cook or wash up, to relax, to pamper yourself. You also go for the food. The food is only part of the reason. If you choose your food in line with your goal of being slim, you can still enjoy all the other aspects of dining out. I'm sure you have friends who dine out often and stay slim, just as you have others who dine out and blame this for their weight gain. It has little to do with the dining out and lots to do with the amount and type of food you choose to eat. Eating out makes a wonderful excuse if you want one, but that is all it is, not a reason.

EVERYTHING I EAT TURNS TO FAT.

Nonsense, metabolic nonsense! At least some of what you eat turns to energy. When there is an excess of this energy it, in turn, is converted to fat. Some people convert food to energy more easily than others. Some convert food into fat more easily than others.

If your metabolism is sluggish, there may be things that can be done to help it. A good naturopath should be able to help you and it is also discussed in the chapter on Supplements. In any case your metabolism is your very own metabolism. It may be more difficult for you to lose weight than for some other people but you can still choose whether you give up and get fat or work at it and get slim. You can choose to be in control of your body or to lie down and be a victim of your metabolism.

DIETS NEVER WORK FOR ME.

Diets work if you do. What you are really saying is that you've tried and failed. By now, having read this far, you should be aware of some of the subconscious reasons why diets haven't worked for you. Now is the time to abandon a thought that is holding you back. Replace it with an affirmation, such as, "Diets do work for me", "I can readily achieve my ideal figure".

I'D HAVE TO GIVE UP THE FOODS I LOVE.

No, don't do that. If you tell yourself that, for the period of the diet, you will give up your favourite food totally, you are also tacitly promising yourself that when the dieting period is over, you *can* have these favourite foods. This may well mean that as soon as you stop the diet, you go out and celebrate on those foods and on goes the weight again.

In the section on Dos and Don'ts we will have more to say on this but here are two thoughts to start with. Firstly, consider changing your favourite foods. After all, it is up to you which foods you decide to put at the top of the favourite list. The top of my list used to be sweets and now it is salads. It is all a matter of what you choose to think.

Secondly, it is not only the nature of the food that affects your weight, but the amount you eat. If you absolutely adore avocados and can make a meal of them and are convinced you can't face a future without them then incorporate them into your new eating pattern, but only have a small amount. You can enjoy the flavour of a quarter of an avocado diced through a salad just as much as a whole one eaten on its own.

If you are so addicted to your favourite food that, once started, you can't stop, see an allergist. Otherwise, don't rule it out totally but have small amounts occasionally.

IT'S BORING.

Diets are often less boring than your usual eating pattern.

Margaret insisted that dieting bored her stiff. Each week she would decide to eat less. She would go home full of promises and then return to my office a week later at which time we'd find that her weight had not changed, nor had she eaten sensibly. The answer was, "Oh, it's so boring, I can never stick to it". Ironically, when I questioned her on her normal eating pattern, it transpired that she had exactly the same breakfast every day, toast and coffee, and the same lunch, a cheese and ham sandwich. It was only her dinner that varied. On her chosen weight-loss programme she had several different breakfasts and lunches to choose from. Boredom was not the problem; it was the excuse.

THERE'S NO POINT, THE WEIGHT COMES BACK ON AGAIN.

How about that for defeatism? Yet, in a way it's true. It's especially true if you consider yourself to be on a diet until you reach the weight you want and think that you can then go back to your old eating pattern. It's that old eating pattern that put the weight on in the first place, so naturally it will do so again. The trick is to change your eating habits on a long-term basis, as we will discuss later in the chapter on Dos and Don'ts. This way you never revert to your old eating pattern and you can maintain the weight loss once you achieve it.

YOU HAVE TO BE HUNGRY ALL THE TIME.

There are two aspects to this. Firstly, welcome hunger. For every moment that you are hungry, your body is having to break down fat cells to create energy. The longer you can be hungry, the more fat is broken down. This should not be taken too far or you will binge on the next meal when you do eventually eat. Secondly, you can avoid being hungry by eating filling but low calorie foods such as salads and vegetables. These fill up your stomach and create a feeling of fullness.

You can also reduce the hunger pangs by keeping your blood sugar levels steady. To do this, avoid sugars at all costs. Eating a candy bar sends your blood sugar level rocketing and then crashing. In the crash phase, when it is below normal, you will feel tired and hungry and be tempted to eat more. Instead of sugar, have some complex carbohydrate such as rolled oats, brown rice or wholemeal bread in small amounts. These will break down slowly in the digestive system and release a slow and steady trickle of glucose molecules (from which all starch is made) into the blood stream, thus helping you to maintain normal blood sugar levels.

IT'S TOO DIFFICULT.
Nothing is difficult but thinking makes it so. Dieting is not too difficult. It may be too much trouble but that is a value judgement you must make for yourself. If you truly do not wish to make the effort to be slim, don't try; you are only setting yourself up for failure.

IT TAKES TOO LONG.
Isn't that lucky. If, by eating less for only one week you could lose 10 kilograms in weight, just think how fast you would gain extra weight when you overate by the same amount of food. It took months, possibly years, to put the weight on so you can hardly expect it to come off in a week.

I THINK I'LL JUST EAT LESS, I DON'T NEED TO DIET.
If you can do it, fine. In fact that is what a lot of this book is about. Once you really do just eat less you will inevitably find your weight goes down.

Kathy said this to me as she sat across the desk in my office. She had come in because her weight was bothering her, she was getting varicose veins and her blood pressure was up. We talked for a while about the different things she could do to lose weight but I could see her eyes glazing over. Eventually she said she didn't need a diet. She knew about foods and about what to eat so she could do it herself. All she needed was something for her varicose veins and something for her blood pressure.

Of course, she knew what to eat. She had been reading about diets in every woman's magazine for the past twenty years. She'd read every book in the library on weight loss and she knew the name of every diet. That led us to the question, "Then why haven't you lost weight already?" In the end she decided to do the "Choosing Weight Intentionally" workshop and she found the answers there. After that she could indeed do it herself because she did know what to eat and she was able to put her knowledge into practice and trim down to her target weight. By losing the weight, her blood pressure went down and by changing her diet her varicose veins improved.

So now you are beginning to get the picture. All of these are excuses, not reasons. They can all be made to apply if you want to hang on to your present weight or if you want a justification for not going ahead, for not achieving. Equally, they can all be surmounted and done away with the moment you decide you are serious about wanting to lose your extra weight.

YOUR WILLPOWER

What normally happens when you go on a weight-loss diet? You promise yourself you will eat less, give up certain foods, exercise more and do whatever else that particular regime demands and none of these actions come naturally. If they did, you would not need to commit yourself to doing them. So to keep the commitments, you have to use the mental force called willpower. But here's where the trouble starts.

Let's assume that the diet you have chosen bans sweets. You repeat to yourself "I will not eat sweets", "I will not eat sweets". After a while, all your subconscious hears is " . . . eat sweets", " . . . eat sweets" and before you know it your mind is focused on sweets and it triggers you to eat them. The more you are determined not to eat something, the more you want to. The more you are determined not to eat, the more you think about food. You set up a duel between what you cannot have and what you want to have. One of the problems with using force and willpower is that you focus strongly on the food and drink you shouldn't have. This attention to forbidden foods can often result in your eating more of them, not less.

Using willpower rarely works because you can exercise willpower for only so long. The time inevitably comes when you relax and then what? Before you know it, all the rules have been broken and you have let down your guard. Another problem is that the minute you come off the diet, either because you reach your ideal weight or simply because you give up, you feel entitled to eat those forbidden foods. You have used your willpower, you have been good and avoided your favourite foods. Now, you think you deserve a reward, and what better reward than something forbidden. The next thing you know, the weight has started to come back and you say "Here we go again, the same old merry-go-round. I'll never manage to be slim or stay slim so what's the point of trying?" Willpower is not the answer. There are much easier ways to lose weight.

The same is true if you are underweight, although willpower is usually less of an issue than for the overweight. It is usually harder to resist the foods you want to eat than to force yourself to eat when you don't want to. You think that if you force yourself to increase your food intake and maintain this eating pattern, you can gain weight and keep it on but when you relax, you go back to your old eating pattern and the weight falls off. If this is the problem for you, then you, too, have found that willpower does not work. You will also find that the other methods given in this book such as discovering why you are thin, and unravelling your emotional background are much easier methods to use than willpower. With these new techniques, you will be able to put on the wanted weight and keep it on.

FOOD AND EATING

If you are underweight rather than overweight, this section is specifically for you. In previous sections you will have learned a lot about yourself. You may also have found some valuable ideas in the section on diet and dieting, since underweight people also eat and don't eat for a variety of emotional reasons. However, you have your own particular problems, or so it probably seems to you. It is worth noting that often the underlying cause is much the same for the overweight as for the underweight. Only the result is different.

Do you hate to eat? Is eating a bore? Do you feel you have to force food down or do you eat all before you and still stay thin? Just as many overweight people underestimate the amount they eat, many underweight people overestimate the amount they eat.

Don and Belinda had been married for fifteen years. In that time Belinda's weight had gradually crept up the scale to a point where she was at least 19 kilograms (3 stone) overweight, in spite of repeated attempts at dieting. Don had stayed as slim as a rake. They ran a family business and this meant that they ate nearly all their meals together. Belinda complained that she ate only half the amount Don ate but, although they were approximately the same height, Belinda gained and Don stayed thin.

When we analysed their daily routine we found that Don had three meals a day, and that was it. They were good meals, not excessive, but not small. Belinda had the same three meals, half size. But that wasn't all. Belinda nibbled all day long, between meals, while she was preparing meals and while she was clearing the meals away. Don did not like to nibble. He did not feel tempted to stop work for a cup of coffee and add a couple of biscuits. In fact his coffee was black and without sugar whereas Belinda's had milk and sugar. He did not eat peanuts with his pre-dinner drink. He did not buy an ice cream on the beach on Saturdays. He just had his three meals.

Cecelia's problem was different. She was painfully thin and complained about her weight constantly to her unsympathetic overweight friends. She swore she ate huge meals, that meals took up a major part of her day, that she didn't have time to eat any more, nor could she fit any more food in. I sympathised until we had a meal together. I had never seen anyone take such small mouthfuls and take so long to chew them. She took fifteen minutes eating a slim sandwich. Clearly, she was grossly underestimating her total food intake. You too may be eating less than you realise.

Run the phrase, "Something eating means to me is . . . " and find out what you get. Nancy did this and here are some of the completions she came up with after the usual ones such as "food", and "being nourished": they included "wasting time", "not being able to get on with things", "making an effort", "struggling".

As a child, Nancy had wanted to do everything, go everywhere, explore everything, read every book, talk to every new person. She was athletic and loved to be active. Mealtimes had been an interruption. She had to be dragged away from a book, a game or a group of friends to go and have her meal. Meals in her family were long, drawn out affairs. Her parents had insisted the whole family sat down to each meal, that they take time, relax, eat slowly and talk. Meals were the time the family came together, where issues and ideas were discussed, where the children learned about the adult world. As they grew up the children were encouraged to discuss politics, art, history and current affairs. To Nancy the meals seemed to be endless. Her attitude to them, that they were interruptions to all the things she wanted to do, persisted into her adult life, even though she could now have eaten more quickly. Instead, she avoided them when she could and she was thin.

Julie's attitude to meals was different. When she ran the

phrase "Something eating means to me is ... " She got "tension", "trouble ... ", "waiting for an explosion". Her father had been an alcoholic with unpredictable moods. The children kept out of his way as much as possible but he could not be avoided at mealtimes. It seemed to Julie, in retrospect, that she had sat through every meal in a state of tension, waiting for her father's violent temper to erupt. She had eaten, but with her stomach in such a knot that she had absorbed little of what she ate. Even now, in her twenties, she found herself tense at mealtimes and had trouble digesting her food. Realising this, she agreed to do some relaxation exercises before meals and this helped solve her problem, but the real advance came when she worked on her relationship with her father.

Just as overweight people blame a lot of their weight on their glands, many underweight people blame their digestion. It may be true that you don't digest food properly and this can be attended to. But the digestive system is one of the first parts of the body to be affected by emotional tensions and resolving these can also help you to gain weight.

PART FOUR:
TOOLS

TOOLS

So far you have learned a lot about your past. At various points along the way you have been told to do exercises and to use certain tools. For convenience, and to avoid spoiling the flow of the information, these exercises and tools have been collected together here.

This is where you will learn how to "run a phrase" in such a way that you can discover many of your subconscious belief systems. You can also find out about affirmations, how you have been using them and how you can make more use of them in the future. The television technique and the use of visualisations is explained and you will find out why, as any dieter knows, willpower doesn't work, not, at least, in the long-term.

If you have been redirected to this point from another section in the book, read the appropriate part, such as how to run a phrase, then return to where you were and continue working through.

These exercises and tools can be used for many different purposes. Here we are particularly interested in using them to help you deal with your weight problem. Running a phrase may help you to learn more about your eating habits and your attitude to food and eating. Affirming you are slim can help you to lose weight. The television technique can help you to avoid a binge, and visualising yourself the weight you want to be can help you stick to your goals. Use them well. They only work if you want them to.

RUNNING A PHRASE

Throughout this book you have seen the term "running a phrase" because it is a useful way to discover what is going on in your subconscious. This is how you run a phrase.

The phrase you are told to run may be simple. It is

usually short and you have been asked to complete the sentence over and over again. We will start with a simple and appropriate phrase, one you have probably said to yourself many times, "I can't lose weight because . . . ". Say it once, complete it and write down the completion. Then do this again. Repeat the process until your responses become repetitive but don't give up. Continue for a while because there may well be some valuable bits of information your subconscious is ready to release.

There is a certain hypnotic power about the phrase itself. It's as if it occupies your conscious mind and takes its attention away from monitoring what you are going to say next. Your subconscious is then free to let out little whispers of underlying truth. The results may look like this:

- I can't lose weight because — I can't resist food.
- I can't lose weight because — of my glands.
- I can't lose weight because — I have to eat what the family eats.
- I can't lose weight because — I get bored and unhappy.
- I can't lose weight because — going on a diet makes me feel deprived.
- I can't lose weight because – of my sweet tooth.
- I can't lose weight because — I'm scared.
- I can't lose weight because — I might get hurt.

It is important that the completion is short and carries no explanation. If, after the first one, "I can't resist food", you had continued with . . . "I enjoy it, and need it, after all you have to eat to stay alive and it's good for you . .", you would have lost the benefit of the process. You would have gone into justification, logic and the conscious brain's ingrained pattern of intellectually justifying everything. By returning to the starting phrase each time, you will get more useful results and a true window into your sub-conscious for buried memories.

This was what Geraldine got by doing the process. At first, her responses were logical and commonplace. They were the reasons many people give for not being able to lose weight such as loving food, blaming their glands, other people's eating patterns, being bored and having a sweet tooth. Then, as she relaxed into the process, her subconscious came up with two more, "I'm scared" and "I might get hurt".

When you get something useful and interesting like that, it is worth exploring it. Geraldine was told to run the phrase "Something I'm scared of is . . . ". When she did, she came up again with several everyday things at the start such as being in a car crash, not having enough money and being lonely. Then she found herself answering " . . . of being conspicuous". It soon became clear that she was afraid to lose weight because she would look better and attract the attention of men and this made her nervous. You can see what a useful tool running a phrase can be.

You may find you get several different bits of information. Keep going with the one phrase until you have a large number of responses. Then, choose the one that seems a little disconnected as we did above, shape a phrase around it and run it. You may then take one of these responses and run a third phrase, and so on. When that is complete, go back to another of the original completions. In Geraldine's case we ran "Something I'm scared of is . . . " until we had milked it dry. We followed up on " . . . being conspicuous" by running the phrase "A way I would be conspicuous is . . .". When we had finished that one, we went back to the last of her completions " . . . I might get hurt". She ran the phrase "A way I could get hurt is . . . "until we had taken it to its conclusion. By the time we had finished we had a pretty good idea of many of the emotions and thoughts that made up Geraldine's attitude to food and to her own body weight and shape.

When you run a phrase, you will be surprised at the results. They will help you in your bid to become slim or gain needed kilograms. They will almost certainly change your life for the better in other ways, too.

Consider the results John came up with. When he ran the phrase "Something dieting means to me is . . . " he listed several completions and then the phrases "being controlled" and "being manipulated". He then ran the phrase "Being controlled means I'm . . . " and got completions that included "weak, helpless, unimportant". It was this last one that really hit home. He would never have guessed that he associated going on a diet with feelings of inadequacy. He decided to take stock of his life and he started working on his self-esteem. He read books and did the personal growth workshop ("Choosing Health Intentionally"). He says his life has totally changed. What started out as a bid to lose weight had set him on the path to a new and much more exciting future.

Here is a clear example of the way your mind works. If you try to analyse the situation logically to find out why you are overweight and why dieting has failed, you will almost certainly run into your old coverup thoughts. When you allow the subconscious mind to throw out information, you can learn a lot.

Betty is another example. She was in the "Choosing Weight Workshop", thoroughly enjoying herself, excited about what she was learning and optimistic that she would go home and lose her excess weight easily. The happy conviction that everything is under control is a workshop situation I have come to suspect, and rightly so. Betty demonstrated that often there is more to come. Up to then we had talked about many of the things that are described in this book but we had not talked much about food or about dieting. Midway through the second morning, "dieting" was on the agenda. Betty was sitting in the front row and I saw her becoming fidgety. Suddenly, she said, "I feel like screaming". When I said "OK, go ahead and scream", she did into a towel that was provided to muffle the noise.

When the outburst was over, I asked what was upsetting her. She didn't know so I had her run the phrase "The thing that made me angry was . . . " and we found that it hinged on the word "dieting". She had been fine when she had thought about her past and her emotional responses. She had enjoyed unravelling some of her biography and recognising some reasons for her behaviour now in her daily life. But once the word "dieting" came up, all her old programmes were activated and unpleasant emotions began to emerge.

The next phrase she was told to run was "Something dieting means to me is ... " and after we got over all the usual ones such as "eating less food", "boredom", "going without", we got to "not having enough", at which point she began to cry. We persisted through her tears since we were clearly getting somewhere and I said, "enough what?" The answer was "money". Her earliest memories were of being cold, not having enough to eat and knowing that it was because there was no money. Since then, eating had become reassurance to her that she was no longer poor. After that we both knew that she could go home, eat only when hungry and that she would lose her excess weight and this is exactly what happened.

Use the technique of running a phrase whenever you are asked to in this book. You can also use it whenever you choose and under any circumstances. For instance, if you are getting angry in a particular situation, run, "The reason I'm angry is ... ", "Another reason I'm angry is ... ". Note the slight change in wording for the second and subsequent repeats of the original phrase. You may be with friends enjoying a chat and feel yourself becoming anxious. Run the phrase "A reason I'm getting anxious is ... ", "Another reason I'm getting anxious is ... ". Remember, you are never upset for the reason you think.

AFFIRMATIONS

Throughout this book you have found examples of affirmations, positive thoughts you can use to change the way you are, think and feel. It is worth pausing a moment here to give more consideration to the concept of affirmations.

Firstly, humans have been making affirmations since time began. The tribal fighters gearing themselves up for battle, stomping round the campfire were affirming to themselves that they were brave and strong and would win the coming battle. Even animals do it. Elephants pawing the ground before they charge are affirming their power and intent. Sports psychologists use visual affirmations when they make a player watch a correct movement repeatedly before they go into action. "You can do it" to a friend is an affirmation.

Affirmations have been used by psychologists and healers for a long time and have become increasingly popular since the beginning of this century. Many books have been written about them and their use. Many people think they are only a part of the recent personal growth movement, but they have a much longer history. You make affirmations to yourself all the time and always have done. Saying such negative and unhelpful things to yourself as "Oh, don't be so stupid", "Gosh I'm fat", "This diet will never work" or "Diets don't work for me", is not using affirmations. These are negative thoughts.

Affirmations include such things as "I can lose weight easily", "I like only the foods that keep me slim", "I can stick to any diet I choose", "I can easily gain the weight I want", "I am rapidly reaching my ideal weight". Be sure that you use affirmations and not negations. When you concentrate on "I'm not hungry", you simply keep the word "hungry" ringing in your ears. This will soon turn to thoughts of food. Similarly "I hate chocolate", will keep the word "chocolate" in your mind with potentially devastating results.

Walking past cake and sweet shops is another example. If you keep saying to yourself that you would love to go inside and purchase some of the produce, but you won't, or "I'd love to but I mustn't", you are reinforcing your old unhelpful beliefs and relying heavily on willpower to see you through. The moment you relax, you're gone: you stop, turn into the shop and start eating.

There is a way around this and Kate did it. She decided

that every time she walked past a sweet shop she would say "Ugh, junk food, yuk". This may be inarticulate but it worked. She created an image for herself of horrid gluggy syrup and dark brown fat clogging up her body, her blood vessels and her skin, so it was easy for her to keep walking past the shop and not be tempted. She then extended this habit to cake shops and tempting counters in supermarkets. Finally, it became automatic at the fast food shops, pizza parlours, bakeries, ice-cream stands and anywhere else she saw food that would hinder her on the path to the slim Kate she wanted to be.

Peter took it another step further. After he pictured the fats and sugars glugging up his system he would say to himself "I'd love some fresh fruit", "I'd love some fresh fruit". By focusing on what would help him towards his goal of losing weight, he had "fresh fruit" ringing in his ears and was able to stick to a helpful eating programme and easily reach his target weight.

If you are too thin, then use affirmations such as "I love food", "I enjoy food", "I readily absorb all the good food I eat".

Most of your thoughts are affirmations of one kind or another. Make them positive and they will work for you.

VISUALISATIONS

You know now that your mind is a powerful tool and have learned some of the things it can do for you. Much of what your mind did at a particular time in the past may have been appropriate then, but it may not be appropriate now.

The good thing about this amazing power of your mind is that you can harness it to help you create your future. It will do this anyway. It will either create your future along the lines of the past and you will go in the direction in which you were headed before you started this book. Or, if you choose to *change* the direction, you can choose to consciously reshape the future and make it what you really want.

We have talked about affirmations. Creative visualisation is, in a sense, a visual affirmation and is one more aspect of using mind power to achieve your goals. Sick people have visualised themselves well; they may have pictured their defence cells gobbling up the bacteria or viruses of the infection, or they may have pictured new cells growing as a wound heals. People have visualised parking spots for cars, green traffic lights, an empty table at a restaurant and other conveniences for themselves. They have visualised exciting relationships, happy outcomes to meetings and winning at sports. Sports psychologists recognise that winning at a particular sport may be as little as 20 per cent skill and as much as 80 per cent mental determination with conviction that you can and will win and the ability to see yourself in the winner's box.

If others are doing it successfully, why not you? Having read this suggestion, you may immediately start to sabotage yourself by saying that you're no good at visualising things, that you can't even decorate a room and have it come out the way you expected, that clothes you think will look great on you often do not suit you at all. Be courageous.

As a baby you were born with a wonderfully creative imagination. All children have it; they love stories and conjure up amazing pictures to go with the words they are hearing. If they are spared their alphabet and their numbers for long enough, this imaginative faculty can be nurtured. If they are spared television they can create their own images. But if you were sent off to school early and praised for academic learning, your creative imagination got pushed into the background. However, like any other faculty, it is only a matter of practice. Get it out, dust it off, and use it.

For most people their creative capacity is largely visual. However, some people have trouble creating pictures in their mind but can easily create sounds. Other people have trouble with both of these but can readily create feelings. Work with the medium that suits you best, but also practise the others. You can put this creative visualisation to work to change your weight and your shape. Start to picture yourself the weight and shape you want to be. If you are currently overweight, be sure you recognise that it is only your body that is overweight and not the inner core of you. You are really a slim person in a body that is too large.

Picture the clothes you will wear as you reach your ideal weight. Create a movie of the way your activities will change, the different way you will move, how much easier it will be to bend over, to touch your toes, to twist, to climb stairs and so forth. As you do this, you will find yourself behaving as a slimmer person, eating less and speeding the process. Add to the effect by consciously holding in your abdominal muscles, pulling your shoulders back, holding your head up. All these things will help to make you feel good about yourself and will speed the process.

If you are about to go to a restaurant with friends and are afraid you will pick fattening foods, do this exercise first. Sit down quietly somewhere and close your eyes. Picture yourself entering the restaurant, smiling and looking relaxed. You look straight ahead to your table — not sideways searching for the dessert trolley. See yourself as you sit there, quietly relaxed rather than snatching at the menu. Decide on the food that will be appropriate for you. Then, see yourself eating that and *only* that. Picture the salad you will start with, the lightly grilled fish and vegetables and see yourself declining dessert. If you know your friends will want dessert, choose to see yourself sitting back relaxed and talking to them while they have their sweets. Finish, by watching yourself stand up to leave, still looking slim, while the others moan about the extra kilograms they will have to work off. Add to this by being aware of the appropriate feelings and sounds that form part of this visualisation.

If you want to gain weight, you will simply change the film. Watch yourself entering the restaurant and eagerly scanning the menu. See the pleasure on your face as you order your meal and then watch as you have an extra course, one more than your usual habit. Be aware that you have eaten well, are satisfied and enjoyed the experience.

You can use this technique for any situation in which you think you may do something you don't really want to do, something that is not in accord with your long-term goal of achieving your ideal weight, even if it is in accord with a short-term goal of brief pleasure.

The more you visualise the desired outcome, the easier it will be to achieve it.

THE TELEVISION TECHNIQUE

It is all too easy to focus on what hasn't worked, on what you can't do and why you won't succeed but it's stupid and counter-productive when you are trying to achieve your goals. It's like trying to climb Mount Everest while you are anchored to the sea floor. Far better that you focus on what you can do than on what you can't do. Focus on what you have done well rather than on your failures. Many people find this difficult because there is always that little voice that insists you are fooling yourself if you try to think well of what you have done. It keeps piping up and reminding you of the times you failed.

Here is a way for you to be conscious of and empowered by your successes. You can use this technique, as you can use the other techniques offered in this book, for weight-loss and weight-gain and also for dealing with almost any other situation in your life.

Go somewhere quiet and sit down on your own. Visualise in your mind all the things you have done of which you are proud. Focus on one thing in particular. It may be the month when you exercised regularly. See yourself getting up in the morning, putting on your running clothes, leaving the house and going for that fifteen-minute run. Be aware of the colours, the sights of all you could see. Feel what it was like as you breathed the new morning's air and how, as your body started to respond, your breathing increased. Be conscious of your sense of self-worth and achievement. Listen for the early morning sounds you could hear. While you have this image in your mind, play with the knobs on your internal television set. Make the picture brighter, the colours stronger and the volume louder. Focus strongly on the way you felt pleasure and satisfaction in what you were doing. Replay this video with maximum clarity and volume and do this as many times as you like. Make the image larger until it fills your entire consciousness. Then, let that picture fade.

Now, re-create the morning you lay in bed and refused to get up but, this time, play with the television knobs in the opposite direction. Make the colours paler and grayer. Shift the focus so that the picture is hazy and harder to see. Turn the volume down so you can barely hear it and then make the picture smaller and smaller until you can hardly see it. Then quickly switch back to the big, bright image of the good time, that time when you were exercising.

Switch back and forth between these two images, spending longer concentrating on the positive image and less time on the negative one. You will soon learn to focus on what you can do, not what you can't do. Use this television technique to focus on the times when you have stuck to your diet and diminish the time when you overate. It is good to do this to avoid feeling guilty and to build your confidence and self-esteem. You are reprogramming your subconscious from the belief that you can't achieve your goals to the belief that you can.

If you apply this technique to yourself and to your attempts to change your weight, you will get your life into a beneficial perspective, one that helps you in your quest for a new body.

PART FIVE:
THE FUTURE

CREATING THE FUTURE YOU

We have come a long way. You have learned a lot about your past and present, about the ways you react to situations, and about some of your beliefs and habits in regard to food and eating. You have learned a lot about why you eat or do not eat and why you treat yourself the way you do. You have also found some tools for learning more about yourself. The technique of running a phrase is something you can use any time in the future to find out more about yourself. If you do the expanded running and turn some of the completions into new phrases to run, you can learn even more.

Now the time has come to put this all together and you are ready to start to create the future you want. Let's move on and start on the steps towards the new you.

- You must feel good about yourself and learn to love yourself. In our society you are taught from a very young age to belittle yourself, to put yourself down. You are taught to be modest, to insist that other people are better than you, and that it is unacceptable to boast of your achievements. In the guise of caring for others and allowing them to go first you also learn that you come last. As little children the message seems clear: you are not as important or as likeable or as loveable as the people around you. We also hear far more criticisms than compliments, thus you hear criticisms of yourself and you develop your own criticisms of yourself. All this makes it difficult to think well of yourself, to love yourself and to feel you deserve to reach your goals and to be the weight you want to be.

  Learning to love yourself is important, it must be taught and practised. It must be achieved, otherwise you will not feel you deserve the goals you have set yourself and you will not achieve them. This is possibly the hardest thing to do and so the following steps are aimed at helping you reach this target.

- You must let go of the past. Your past habits, mental, emotional and physical, have got you where you are, with the body you have now. Since you are reading this book you almost certainly do not feel that you are perfect the way you are at the moment, and in the shape you would like to be for the rest of your life. Learn to let go of all that is holding you back, then you can make the changes that will enable you to move on to the future you want.

  As part of letting go of the past, you have to learn to forgive the past, particularly the people you blame for your present state. This almost certainly means forgiving your parents for things they did that made your childhood less than perfect. There will be a lot of other people to forgive as well, but parents are especially important. This forgiving can be done not because you are better than them and not because they were wrong. Being right or wrong does not come into this. You resent them for what they did, not because it was wrong. You might resent your family's financial circumstances, you might resent your father for leaving home or your mother for disciplining you. You forgive them not for their sake, but for your own, so you can leave your past behind.

- Get rid of self-pity. Being over- or underweight can be a wonderful reason to feel sorry for yourself. You can get attention and sympathy, and you have excuses for all sorts of things. Stop feeling sorry for yourself, you don't need this any more.

- Learn to say no, not just to food, this is only a reflection of your life overall. Learn to say no, when it is appropriate, in all aspects of your life. This may seem easy but, as you will learn, from an early age you were programmed to say yes far more readily than no.

- Learn more about yourself, come to a fuller understanding of yourself, your needs and your motivation and develop your intuition. You have made a start if you have read this far, there is still more you can do.

- Develop your self-confidence. This is not the same as loving yourself but it is certainly a part of it.

- Finally, we come full circle, back to learning to love and approve of yourself and to be proud of yourself. Now that you have accomplished the above you can truly like and love yourself and, what's more, feel good about doing so. You can also do this in a way that is appropriate to the society in which you live and in a way that is comfortable for the people in your life.

If you're ready, let's move on and start on these steps towards the new you.

SELF-ESTEEM OR LOVE OF SELF

We could have called this section all sorts of things. Initially, it was headed simply "self-love". Do you love yourself? Does the question make you uncomfortable? Lots of people think that loving themselves, and acknowledging that, is akin to boasting.

Mary's reply was "Well, I would if I wasn't so fat, and if I didn't get irritable and if . . . " and I heard a list of criticisms about herself. No-one with such a poor self-image would be likely to feel they could succeed or that they deserved to succeed.

Jeremy is another example. He sat, or drooped, in his chair in my office. My previous patient had taken much more than his allotted time and so Jeremy had been kept waiting. Many people get impatient when this happens, and are keen to get on with things. Not Jeremy. He indicated that I was not to hurry for him as his needs were not important. Later I found that he thought he was a failure, could never be any good at anything. He was anxious and depressed, had headaches and all sorts of digestive upsets.

Jeremy was married, with two children, and worked long hours to give his family a better lifestyle. He blamed his own inadequacies for not being able to give them more. He'd taken time off from his work to see me because his wife had insisted and he wanted to please her. He seemed anxious that I should understand this and that he would not have taken time off for himself. As we talked, it became obvious that he felt he had to do things for others as it would be wrong to do things for himself. When I asked him if he liked himself, he looked up startled and confused. He first said "No", then "Well, yes, but no". He didn't think he was bad, he didn't feel he could say he disliked himself but he was incapable of saying he liked himself. When I suggested he could try loving himself he was even more confused.

He explained that all his life he had been told not to be conceited, not to boast and not to think himself better than other people. The liturgy had come from parents who were determined to bring him up with good manners until now, as an adult, he could not even begin to acknowledge his own worth. Jeremy is hardly unusual. Ask anyone if they love themselves and there is a good chance that they will go into shock. You know yourself better than anyone. You know what you show the world and what other people see of you. You also know what goes on inside the parts you don't always show. You alone know that. When you sum it all up, you reach a conclusion. Either you like yourself, that is, you are likeable, or you don't, that is, you're not so nice. The conclusion you reach is then shown to the world. Other people are aware of the conclusion you express, and they will, by and large, take you at face value.

Think of someone you know who is popular with lots of self-confidence and assurance. They feel good about themselves and expect other people to like them. Tacitly, they have told the world they are likeable. The fact that they are at ease and comfortable with themselves clearly shows and becomes shared by everyone.

When a child experiences an achievement and runs to mother with a glow on its face saying, "Look what I've done", they are rejoicing in their achievement in this new world. If this happens when other people are present and the child is rebuked, the first step has been taken to impress that child that its behaviour is wrong. Is this what happened in your childhood?

Can you feel comfortable saying "I love myself?" Could you say it aloud to someone else? Go ahead, try it and imagine yourself saying it. Do your toes curl up? Do you feel uncomfortable? Do you feel embarrassed?

Let's turn to self-esteem. It sounds dry, compared to loving yourself. Yet you may feel more comfortable with this. Somehow, it is all right to have self-esteem, a cool and intellectual estimation of your worth but it's not so acceptable to have self-love.

To create your future the way you want with the figure you want, you have to feel comfortable with yourself, convinced that you are worthwhile and care enough about yourself to make the necessary changes. You have to feel you deserve the time and energy it takes to ensure that your lifestyle and habits are appropriate to achieving the looks you want. You have to be able to tell the world that you deserve to look good and that you think well enough of yourself to have taken the trouble to achieve it.

Many people with low self-esteem hide behind a large body. By being large, they think they can escape attention and have permission to opt out of situations so they needn't try. They have something to blame for their low self-esteem.

Other people go to the other extreme. They become very thin, as if by being thinner, they can disappear. They may feel that by being thin, they avoid being assertive. They are taking up less space and they are less likely to be in the way and be noticed. They can't hide but they can try.

You can choose to alter or influence what the world sees but you do have to show it something. If that something is false, then living with that pretence is going to cause you problems. It is far simpler to value yourself 100 per cent for being exactly what you are. If there are things you want to change, that's fine. Go ahead and start the changing process but love your Self for that, too.

LETTING GO OF THE PAST

We all have things in our past that we wish weren't there. No-one's past was perfect or exactly the way they say they would have liked it to be. Yet, at another level that says we are responsible for our lives and created everything in it, it was indeed perfect. Some of your complaints about your past are minor. You may have wished you had done better at school, had been better at sport, wished you'd had more money or less acne, more excitement or less trouble. These are minor regrets or resentments and you may think about them, but don't spend a lot of energy on them. Some of your resentments and complaints about your past are more serious. You may have wished for different parents, different family, different skills, more money, a closer family, more freedom, more or less siblings, less cruelty or a different life altogether.

There is no objective classification of resentments. What may be a minor resentment to you may be a major resentment to someone else. What counts is the way you react.

It is common to hang on to old resentments. People say, "If only so and so hadn't happened or been done to me, my life would have been different", or, "It's because of so and so that I'm the way I am". Blaming other things and other people in your past for the way things are now means you are refusing to take responsibility for your own life. For as long as you do this, it will be impossible to change the present into the future you want. Telling your subconscious you are not responsible for your past tells it that you weren't in control at the time. This, in turn, says you can't be in control of the present or the future. If you can't control your life, then what's the point in trying to change things? The whole business of resenting and blaming the past weakens your attempts to take control of your future and your weight and all the future habits that will affect it.

The issue is not whether you actually did create each event in your life. It's not a case of insisting you chose your parents, your family, your brains, your schooling and all the events that happened to you. It is a case of being prepared to believe that you could have done so. You may feel that you cannot know whether or not you made these choices. Possibly you did or maybe they just happened to you. If you cannot know for sure whether or not you have chosen or created everything that happened to you, ask yourself, "Which is the more useful belief?" Is it not more useful to believe that you were in control then and are in control now so that you can be in control in the future, rather than believe you are at the mercy of fate? The first step in letting go of the past is to take responsibility for it. Don't feel guilty for any part of it. Just accept it.

If you claim responsibility for all that happens in your life, there are other positive benefits. Let's presume you created your childhood in a way that you thought would be right for you. After all, why would you have created a childhood you didn't want? It is then reasonable to assume that you derived some benefit from the childhood you created no matter how bad it may have seemed.

If you assume you made the perfect childhood for yourself, then discover what you gained from it. Run the phrase, "A benefit I got from my childhood is ... ", "Another benefit I got from my childhood is ... " and see what you get. At first you may feel inclined to focus on the good aspects, those parts that you enjoyed. But, turn your attention to the parts of which you complain. You will find that even the worst part of your past can be seen as generating some benefit. It may seem to have been a pretty tough way to reach that benefit, but it did generate a positive outcome.

Annette told me the story of a drunken father, a family

with barely enough money for survival, where physical violence was common, where she was terrified when the pubs closed and her father would stagger home. She would wake up and help her frightened mother drag him to bed before he got violent.

When she ran the phrase suggested above, she got " . . . I learned to be strong", " . . . I learned I could cope, no matter what" and " . . . I learned to make the most of the good times" as completions. These were pretty good life skills to learn even if learning them was tough.

She then ran the phrase, "A thing I didn't have to cope with as a child was . . . ". She got completions that included ". . . being left out of my parents' shared interests", ". . . having only one parent", " . . . being alone while my mother was out working", " . . . fights with my brother". Focusing on what she got out of her childhood as benefits and becoming aware of the things she hadn't had to cope with, she was able to face the future with confidence and in peace.

Holding on to old resentments means that they will continue to affect you emotionally. It saps your energy that could be better spent on creating the new you. It also makes you feel you are a victim. If you can't let go of these old thought patterns, there's a good chance you won't be able to let go of your old eating patterns or your old body fat.

Make a list of all the people towards whom you feel resentment, however small or large. Include people at home, in your family, at work, people you meet socially and even strangers such as bus drivers or shop assistants. Go right back to your earliest memories and work from there up to the present. List all the people that you feel have harmed you or whom you have blamed for things in your life no matter how small. Then take one of the names or events and list all the possible benefits you derived.

Now you know what you gained from a situation, it is time to let it go, for good. Write down a statement that would clear the situation.

When Betty did this, she came up with the following. "I

resent the man who sold me my car. He must have known it was faulty and it has cost me a lot of money". The statement she made, which is called a release statement, to clear that resentment was "I could have had the car checked but I chose not to spend the money. I take responsibility for this." In this way Betty was able to stop letting resentment eat her up internally. The ulcer healed, her mood lightened and she was able to go ahead and get the car fixed and enjoy it.

Mark's problem was less tangible. He resented his boss for making him stay back and do extra work some evenings, even though there was no question of overtime. After a lot of struggle he came up with the following as his release statement, but he felt he could *not* make it. It was "He had every right to ask me to work back, he's often given me time off when I need it".

Secondly, ask yourself the following questions in relation to this statement, "What would you lose by making this statement?", "What would you gain by making this statement?" and "What do you risk if you don't make this statement?"

Betty felt that if she made the clearing statement she would have to admit she'd been silly, and she didn't want to do that. However, she recognised that she would gain peace of mind if she could let it go. The risk she ran in not making the statement is that she would never enjoy her car and this would affect her adversely every time she got into it, making her cross and irritable. She decided to make the statement and let the matter go.

Mark believed that if he made the release statement he had chosen he would no longer have a reason to feel superior to, and have the right to criticise, his boss. On the positive side, if he did make it, he could relax again and have a better relationship with his boss. If he didn't make it he might be risking his job, since this attitude was making his boss look unfavourably on him. After much soul-searching he decided to make the statement.

There is no need to make the statement to the person involved. After all, it is unlikely that the man who sold

Betty the car had given the matter a second thought once the deal was complete. He wasn't feeling guilty or bothered by her resentment. The only person to suffer was Betty herself.

Mark's boss probably felt he had every right to ask Mark to do a few extra hours. He may well have been surprised if Mark had made the statement to him, taking the view that if Mark didn't like working back perhaps he wasn't suited to the job. However, the change in Mark, once he had made the statement within himself, changed their relationship and both of them benefited.

Do this, yourself. Go through each resentment you have about your past until it is totally clear. There may be some things you can let go and others you feel you must keep. Fine, let the easy ones go and then start working on the harder ones. They all have to go for you to be entirely free from the constraints of the past. You may get through part of your list and then feel it getting easier and that you might as well let it all go in one fell swoop. You can do this. Come up with a statement that encompasses all your past resentments. It might be something like "I take full responsibility for my past and all that happened. I release all old resentments and look forward to the future I create in freedom".

Whatever you do, it is important that you do this exercise and that you write it down. Write the initial list and the clearing statements. If you find you are struggling and having a difficult time doing this exercise, then write down the answer to the three intermediate questions as well. Just thinking it through briefly does not give the same result. Every time a resentment comes to mind, make the appropriate clearing statement until it becomes embedded in your belief system and your actual response to the old memory. You know you have won when all the old negative thoughts drop away.

Another patient who did this told me that she had come to accept her unhappy childhood completely as having been of her own choosing and of benefit to her in several ways. She had become aware of this when, at a family gathering, she met an uncle who had known her as a child. He had begun to commiserate with her about her dreadful childhood. She told me she had been bored, and whereas she once might have revelled in his sympathy, this time she had switched the conversation to other things. This made her realise what a long way she had come in her personal development and that her past was no longer affecting her.

Deciding to forgive someone for something they did is really a decision to stop giving yourself a hard time. Forgiveness is your decision to stop beating yourself up. If you don't forgive, the only person that suffers is you.

Many people find it hard to forgive their parents for the perceived wrongs they experienced. For a long time your parents were the most important people in your life. They were the ones you trusted as responsible for your welfare and they were meant to look after you. That is our common underlying assumption. But, your parents were only human. They had their own issues to deal with, their own uncertainties and resentments. They were far from infallible. You may now be at the age when they had you as a child. From your present wisdom, perhaps you can better understand and forgive their actions. Remember, that these actions may well be actions for which they feel they need no forgiveness; they may feel they did right although you may feel they did wrong. It doesn't matter. What does matter is that you let go of your old resentments and, along with it, you can lose your unwanted weight and everything else that currently shackles you.

Forgive *your Self*, too. It is all too easy to criticise yourself, to run yourself down, to blame yourself. This is not helpful and could, in fact, be considered an indulgence. When you are fretting over something you did in the past, recognise that the thing you did then made sense at the time in the light of your needs at that time. Do not blame yourself. Acknowledge yourself and let it go. If you can do this in relation to past events, it can also take the worries out of the present. When you try to make a decision today, your real concern is whether or not you will look back on this day and kick yourself for what you did. In the future you will have more wisdom and hindsight and you will then know what you should have done. But for today you can only make the decision that you think is the best for today.

Many people deal with their problem by gaining weight and thus proving to themselves how bad they are.

Rebecca had an affair with a married man during her first year at college. When she became pregnant, she panicked and phoned him at home, and as a result his wife found out. Rebecca decided to have an abortion. And then the affair ended. Recently she had started to blame herself for being stupid, for hurting his wife, for having an abortion, and for behaving badly. She turned to food and gained weight.

Rebecca's father had left home when she was six years old, later she herself left home to go to university in a strange town. She didn't want marriage, she wasn't ready for the emotional upheavals of a relationship with a man her own age. She wanted a father figure and comfort, secure in the knowledge that he couldn't marry her and she wouldn't be called on to make such a commitment. The issue is not whether she was right or wrong. The thing had happened. Now she had two choices. She could either continue to feel badly about what she had done and overeat or she could clear up the situation and forgive herself. It was important for her to realise she had done what was best for herself at the time. Now she could lose the unwanted weight.

Now, it's up to you. You can carry around all those old resentments. You can blame everyone else. You can feel miserable and be a victim if you so choose or you can do all the exercises above. Let the past go and get on with your future.

KNOWLEDGE AND UNDERSTANDING

Feeling good about yourself and loving yourself is to understand yourself and to know yourself as fully as you can. You may have thought, before you started reading this book, that you understood yourself pretty well. Yet the chances are that, by now, you have learned more and there may well be even more to learn.

We will start with a supposition. Let us suppose that you are exactly where you have chosen to be. In other words we will accept that all the choices, large and small, made by you throughout your life have culminated in the position you are now in. You may still feel that many of these decisions were imposed on you. Yet, we agree to accept that you elected to be imposed on. At any stage you could have chosen a different future but you didn't.

You can never refuse to make a decision. You either make one actively or by default. It's rather like voting. If you refuse to vote, it is in effect a vote for the party you would not have voted for, had you voted. In the same way, by not making a decision to get out of a situation, however horrible, you, in fact, voted to stay in it.

Janine argued strongly about this suggestion. She had been married to Jack for ten years when she fell in love with another man. She was about to ask Jack for a divorce when he had an accident on the building site where he worked and became a quadriplegic. His parents were dead, they had no children and she came to the conclusion she could not leave him and marry the man she loved as he was virtually helpless. She insisted she had no choice in the matter. But she did have a choice: she could have gone ahead with the divorce, but to her that was unthinkable. Feeling trapped, she began to overeat. Once she realised that she was in a position of her choice, she was able to find other freedoms and stop overeating.

However stark the alternative, there always is one. It may be so stark that you couldn't possibly take it or it may be so stark that you can't even find it but there is one. You make a choice, even if you make one by default. You would rather be where you are now than pay the price to change.

Lynette wanted to travel. She collected travel brochures and dreamed of places she would visit. She nearly drove her husband mad with regrets that she hadn't ever travelled outside her home country. When she thought about it, she realised that if she were to travel, she would have to give up the job she loved and would have to leave Simon behind. Simon had no itchy feet and was busily carving out a successful career. Finally, she realised that, much as she wanted to travel, she wanted her job and Simon more. It came down to the fact that she would have liked to travel but she didn't actually want to enough to pay the price of giving up Simon and her job. She had claimed that she had no choice. She then came to understand that she had made her choice and decided to stay at home. From then on she settled down until such time as she and Simon could travel together.

If you still think there are things you want to do but that you are being stopped by outside forces, realise that there are no great people — there are only ordinary people doing great things. You can do as much as you want if you want to enough. That last is the key phrase, "if you want to enough". If you don't "want to enough" you have decided, if only by default, not to do it.

Perhaps there are things you would like to do but you're afraid to try in case you fail. Yet, if you have never failed at anything, you have never tried. It is said that Edison experimented with 999 light bulbs, none of which worked, before he developed one that did. When someone commented about the 999 failures, he replied that there had been no failures. He had discovered 999 ways that didn't work and one that did.

So, back to where we started. Where you are now is where, given the options available at the time of each decision, you have chosen to be. From this you can learn a great deal about yourself. You may come to recognise that you are single because you are afraid of commitment, that you stay unhappily married because you hate the thought of living alone, that you are not working because you are afraid of the challenge, that you look after elderly relatives because you fear other people's disapproval. Whatever you discover, learn from it and use it now to make the decision to change your weight.

SELF-PITY

Stop feeling sorry for yourself. "But I don't", you cry. Are you sure? Have you ever complained that it's not your fault, it's all in your genes or your metabolism? Have you wished you had a better figure or envied other people who can eat what they like and never gain weight? Have you ever told yourself that it was all right for other people who didn't have to cook family meals or entertain as part of their business, who didn't get bored or lonely and feel that eating was compensation. Have you ever said "If only . . . ", "It's not my fault . . . " and "I can't help it . . . "?

Whatever debits and credits there are in your life, they are your starting point. Accept them. Just like the research that showed that little children had more than ten times as many criticisms as words of praise during a day, I suspect that you give your subconscious a lot more complaints than grateful thoughts. Monitor your thoughts for a day. Discover how much time you spend feeling sorry for yourself and wishing you had more and how little time you spend appreciating what you have.

A colleague told me that he had been wishing for ages that he could move to a better office, that he could live in a larger house and that he could afford to go overseas more than once every couple of years. He thought of the wealthy set, the jet set, he thought of travelling first class to Europe with his family, he thought about being able to live in a waterside house. He said he would know he was successful when he had achieved these things. Then a patient who lived in a small suburban house, had never been outside the country and commuted to work by train came to see him. At the end of the interview they both commented that there were several dreams they would like to achieve. The patient said, "But it's all very well for you, you can afford to live and work here". This simple statement rocked the practitioner back on his heels. He realised that while he had spent much of his time envying the rich and famous, he was living a life that other people envied. He stopped feeling sorry for himself from that point on.

Make a list of all your assets and of all the things you have, however small. Make a list of all the things you can do and enjoy. Be aware of how many people, the world over, would love to be able to have or enjoy some of these things. Never mind that the person next door may be, or may seem to be, better off than you, physically, mentally and emotionally. You are still rich if you choose to see it that way. Everyone can find someone else who is better at something or who has more of something else. The best tennis player in the world can envy someone else's ability with a particular stroke. The wealthiest man can envy another man his wife. We can all find someone to envy if we wish. But why would you want to? Isn't it better to be aware of all that you do have?

After all, it is not important to *be* wealthy but to *feel* wealthy. It is more important to *feel* lucky than to *be* lucky.

Desmond was a clerk in a government office. His work was routine and dull. His home life was neutral — not happy yet not unhappy. He had formed the habit of going to the pub at lunch time, having a pie and a few beers then, and a few more beers on the way home. After dinner he would watch television, have another beer and some peanuts. Most evenings, by the time he went to bed, he was definitely not sober, though he insisted he wasn't drunk. Inevitably the pounds had crept on and now he wanted to lose weight.

Together we planned a diet that could have worked for him. He didn't stick to it. We also planned the sort of moderate exercise he could do. He didn't do it. Instead, over the next two visits, he told me why he couldn't give up his beer, why he couldn't change his job to one he would like better, why he couldn't eat salads at lunch time, why he couldn't exercise, and a great deal more.

Eventually, realising we were getting nowhere, I told him I didn't want to hear another word about what he couldn't do. All I was interested in hearing was what he could do. For the next fifteen minutes he would start a sentence, then as soon as it became negative I interrupted him. The conversation went something like this: "What food can you cut down on?" Well, I could give up the second meat pie, but then . . . " *stop* "What else could you cut down on? " "Well, I suppose I don't need the peanuts after dinner, but I've nothing else . . . " *stop*. When I repeated that I only wanted to hear positive answers he began, not to change, but to realise how negative his thoughts were. By his next visit he had made a big effort to turn his thinking around. In fact he said he was staggered to realise how much he complained. That was his first step.

If you can stop feeling sorry for yourself and start realising how well off you are, you will not be tempted to eat because of a negative emotion such as self-pity.

We come back to an earlier point when we were considering which viewpoint to take, the view that you created your life or the view that you were not in control. It is not a question of whether you are lucky or unlucky. The point is whether you choose to consider that you are lucky or choose to consider you are unlucky. The moment you choose to believe you are lucky, wealthy, happy and so forth, the moment you get rid of self-pity, then that is when you can start feeling positive about your ability to change your weight.

GUILT

Do you feel guilty? Do you spend time telling yourself you should have done this and you shouldn't have done that, and then feeling guilty for your sins and omissions? Some people castigate themselves so much they feel dreadful and then eat for comfort.

Are you always trying to please others, then blaming yourself if you don't? Do you do things to gain approval? Does it work? No, of course not, because you can always find someone who doesn't like something you've done and so are doomed to failure. Many people eat in an effort to deal with this type of unresolved guilt.

Let's take a closer look. If you try to do the right thing, you first need to know what the right thing is. Who is to tell you what is right and what is wrong? Do they know better than you? Why are you letting them decide what is right and wrong for you? What we are talking about is not so much these major rights and wrongs as the many smaller decisions that go into daily living. Should you spend more time with the kids or with your husband? Should you earn more for the family or take more time to be with them? Should you get a job or stay home? Should you please your friends by going to their party or visit your elderly parent? Should you type this report first for one boss or the letters for another boss? Which job on the list waiting to be done should you do first? Do you deserve a new outfit or should the money be spent on something else? Should you go to university and study or get on with earning a living and being independent? Which clothes should you wear? What should you cook for dinner?

These are only a few of the many decisions you make on a daily basis. From the trivial to the important, they are often based on trying to please other people. If you live your life by trying to please others, you are doomed to failure and this can affect your eating habits.

The answer is for you to do what *you* think is right, making the best decision you can at the time and then be prepared to accept the outcome.

Carol had been a successful interior decorator. Then she married Bob and they had three children in four years. By the time their youngest child was two years old Carol felt so trapped by babies, nappies and domesticity that she thought she would go out of her mind. She talked it over with Bob who felt the children still needed their mother at home. He recognised her growing discontent and finally agreed to her going back to work.

They arranged for someone to look after the children. Carol did the shopping in her lunch hour and much of the housework on the weekends. The children were distressed but they got used to the new arrangements. Bob missed the fun weekends they had previously enjoyed but didn't complain. Carol loved her work but felt guilty when she thought what she was doing to Bob and the kids. Yet she couldn't face the thought of giving up her new job. She felt guilty, she became upset, so she ate. Her weight increased, she became depressed, she ate more.

Carol's is a typical pattern. You may start off the guilt process for a variety of reasons but the last part is familiar to lots of overweight people. You start on a packet of biscuits, you feel guilty and so to cheer yourself up you eat the rest of the packet.

Make a list of the things you do to get approval. You will probably get the best results by running the phrase "Something I do to get approval is . . . " or something similar. In a similar way, make a second list of the things you do to avoid incurring other people's disapproval. Thirdly, make a list of the things that make you feel guilty, "Something that makes me feel guilty is . . . ".

If you are having trouble with this one here is an exercise for you to do. Write down your own standards. Establish what is appropriate behaviour for you in any given situation. Then live by them. That way you are free and need not feel guilty and you can eliminate one more reason for emotional eating. Decide that for you sweeping and dusting the house once a week is acceptable and don't feel guilty when it is dusty on the sixth day. Decide that you will be at work on time or that if you are late you will make the time up that same day. Stop feeling guilty. When you arrive at ten past nine on Friday morning, stay back during lunch. Decide that you can have one night a week out with the boys but do something your wife likes on Sunday and stop feeling guilty.

Guilt is a useless emotion. As a child I knew a man who kept telling people how guilty he felt for this and that. Even then it seemed to me that he was using this as an excuse or a justification for whatever it was he did so that he needn't change his behaviour. Guilt is a destructive and also a manipulative emotion. Don't become its victim or try to use it to control others.

If, after a while, you still feel guilty, sit down and work

out why. If you are not sure, run the phrase "A reason I still feel guilty is . . . " until your subconscious lets you know. Then decide what you can do about it, resolve to do it and accept that is all you can do.

Here is another direct and practical way to reduce or eliminate the effect of guilt on your attempts to lose weight. Perhaps you have been putting into practice what you have read here. You have decided to eat less, to work on yourself more, and all goes well for a few weeks. You lose 5 kilograms (11 pounds) and are pleased. Then you go out to dinner and can't resist the rich food. Next morning, horror of horrors, you find you have gained 1 kilogram (2 pounds). You have a couple of options. You may decide you have blown it and you'll never stick with this programme, that you'll not even be able to keep the weight off even if you do manage to get slim. You may feel so bad about the incident, as you dwell on it, that it becomes the horror movie of the year in your mind. The chances are that your attempts at weight loss are doomed, at least temporarily.

Here's a way around this. Go to the section on "Tools" and review the television technique. In this case, bring to mind all the things you did in the good month when you lost 5 kilograms (11 pounds). See and hear yourself refusing second helpings and choosing to eat only what is good for you. Feel what it was like as the weight came off and your clothes got looser. While you have this image in your mind, play with the knobs on your internal TV. Make the picture brighter, the colours stronger, the volume louder, make it larger until it fills your entire consciousness. Then let that picture fade. Now, recreate the evening when you overate. Only this time play with the TV knobs in the other direction. Make the colours paler and grayer. Shift the focus so the picture is hazy, turn the sound down so you can't hear it. Then make the picture smaller and smaller until you can barely see it. Next, quickly switch back to the big, bright image of the good month.

Another way to deal with guilt is to use affirmations. If you persistently feel guilty when you break your diet, yet continue to do so, then see what happens when you affirm "It is OK for me to break my diet once a week". You're going to do it any way, don't heap guilt and ashes on your head as well.

A slightly unexpected result occurred when Denise tried this. She adored chocolate and said she could never lose weight because she could never give it up, and that once she started on one piece she simply had to eat the whole bar. Without telling me she decided to affirm "It is OK to eat chocolate". When she told me about it afterwards she said "You know, a funny thing happened. Because I kept telling myself it was all right to eat it I found I stopped thinking about it. In fact, I really think I lost some of the desire. On the occasions when I did get some I bought only a small bar because I could tell myself it would be all right to buy more later if I wanted. Anyway it worked. I have hardly eaten any and look", as she jumped on the scales, "my weight is down 1.5 kilograms (3 pounds) since last week".

Learn why you feel guilty. That on its own is often sufficient to alleviate the situation. Focus on what works, and your achievements. In these ways you will get things into perspective and find you can continue on your journey to the slim new you.

NO AND YES

SAYING NO

"No and Yes" are two small words with powerful connotations. If your future includes losing weight, you are going to have to eat less and this means saying "No" to food when sometimes you want to say "Yes". It is time to explore the difficulties many people have with saying "No".

Saying "No" seems to be a problem faced by women more than men. As a child, one of the things you had to learn was that you were expected to do as you were told. You were expected to say "Yes" rather than "No". You may have argued with your mother but, by and large, you didn't argue with father. When father said to do something, you probably said "Yes" more often than "No". With mother, the arguments may have been more prolonged but, it is still likely that, in the end "Yes" was the answer.

How do you feel now if you have to say "No"? If someone asks you to do something and you answer "Yes", that is possibly all you will say. If you say "No", you may well feel you have to offer an excuse to make a justification. Is this so for you? Listen to yourself in the next few days and find out. What happens at the dinner table when you are offered more food? Do you say "Yes" because it is easier or more polite than it is to say "No"? You may say "Yes" to be polite and you may also say "Yes" in case you don't get another chance.

Think about what may have happened in your childhood and what may still happen. You have nearly finished your first helping and are offered a second. You gulp down what's on your plate and accept more before your body has had time to register that it has had enough. If you had waited quietly and thought about it for a while, you would have realised that you really had enough and didn't want more. Now, the food is on your plate, you eat it because you feel you should. Does this happen to you? At dinner parties or meals in other people's homes, do you have second helpings because you feel this will show you enjoyed the food, whereas to say "No" would be to suggest that you hadn't enjoyed it? Listen to how many times you and other people, when asked if they would like more, say "No, but it really was delicious", as if "No" would imply they didn't like it.

As an exercise, the next time you dine out with someone, take care to praise the food as extravagantly as is appropriate *before* the end of the course. Then when asked if you would like more, just say "No, thank you" quietly. Imagine youself doing it now as you read this. What happens? Do you feel impelled to add a rider, such as "No thank you, but it was delicious"? If so, you may have a history and a habit of overeating to please someone else. To achieve the new slim you it will be necessary to change this habit. Some people feel that rather than saying "No, but . . . " it is even more polite and complimentary to say "Yes, I shouldn't, but I must, because it tasted so good". By overeating, they are praising the food even more but they are also creating havoc with their figures.

There is another major issue with saying "No" and it relates to the old bugaboo, sex. If you are female, you grew up saying "Yes" to your father about other things whether you felt like it or not. This is commonly translated into a habit and an expectation that you will or should say "Yes" rather than "No" to men in general and agree to all sorts of things you'd rather not do. Women patients often tell me that they agree to doing all sorts of things boyfriends or husbands want simply because they feel they must say "Yes" rather than "No". It's all part of their training, even in the twentieth century.

Many a man has played on this theme in the back seat of the car, in the cinema or on the sofa. It goes a bit like this, "Oh come on, we've come so far you can't say No now". There's plenty of implied guilt there. The same can happen after you're married when a man invites you out for a drink or meal while your husband is away. If you say "No" there's implied guilt when he says "Don't be so unsophisticated. Can't you trust yourself", and the reluctance to say "No", especially to a man, is reinforced.

It is so much easier to be overweight, less attractive and not invited out in the first place and so avoid the problem altogether. If this is the way it is for you then being over-weight is a protection you will need until you can learn to say "No" comfortably. When this aspect of weight manage-ment and its underlying motives is discussed in the clinic, many women deny it. When it comes up during a weekend workshop, where people are probing some of their sub-conscious motives, women find that it is exactly what they are doing.

Being aware of what you are doing is the first step. Changing the pattern is the next. To get around it, practise saying "No". When you feel you can say "No" successfully and comfortably, you will not need to be overweight as a defence.

You will, of course, want to choose your times. There's no point in saying "No" to something you really want to do, just for the sake of practice. Next time you are invited out and don't want to go, instead of going, gently say "No". The world won't blow up. In the same way, learn to say "No, thank you" when invited to have a second helping instead of making an excuse such as "That was delicious but I'm full". As long as you have already praised your hostess, she won't be offended.

If you have trouble saying "No", find out why. Run the phrase "the reason I didn't say "No" was ... " and find out what you get. Another useful phrase to run is "Saying No means ... "

Olivia did this when invited to join some friends for a luncheon party at the races. She said "Yes" and then regretted it. When she was asked to run the first phrase above, she came up with these completions: "I didn't want to hurt their feelings", "I didn't want them to think I was no fun", "I didn't want to be left out in future" — all fairly common ones. Then, she got "so they wouldn't think I couldn't come", "so they wouldn't think I was afraid". "Afraid of whom? " brought the response, "my husband". When she thought it over, she realised she was indeed afraid of her husband. When she thought it over further, she decided she was not so much afraid of *him* as afraid of what *he thought of her*. She found she had been living her life in such a way that he would think well of her and wouldn't do things she didn't like such as moving house, or having his elderly father live with them. The next step was to sit down and discuss the situation with him and it then transpired that he didn't want any of those things either.

Come to terms with saying "No" and you may have beaten a major obstacle to becoming slim.

SAYING "YES"
Saying "Yes" can be as difficult for some people as saying

"No" is for others. Many people who become anorexic say "No" to food because it is an area where they can exercise control. As a child they may have been told to do this, that and the other thing and known that obedience was expected. They may have seen other children in the family want more food and it was refused them. There is no freedom there. But they think if they *refuse* food, they *can* win. It is one way in which they can exert absolute control over their bodies.

Refusing to eat, is a way to get attention. Even small babies know this. There are few mothers who do not get anxious if a child refuses to eat. They will spend endless hours coaxing the reluctant eater and preparing different foods and delivery systems in an effort to make the child eat. Unless you are one of six children with a working mother too busy to notice, you can be sure of attention this way.

Try running the phrase, "A benefit I got from refusing food as a child was ... ". Another useful one to run is "Saying Yes means ... ". When Geoffrey did this, he got "... I'm obeying other people", " ... I'm doing what I'm told" and " ... I'm not free". He told me that he had had a very strong-minded mother, and that his wife was the strong person in their marriage. She made the decisions regarding the children, money, where they would live and so forth. He felt she was usually right and he didn't like to refuse her or stand up to her when his opinion differed from hers.

A woman can often say "No" in bed as a form of rebellion, of exerting independence and freedom. For a man this is usually self-defeating and certainly would have been so for Geoffrey. The only way he felt he could refuse his wife or disagree with her was in regard to his eating habits. Refusing much of the food she prepared was his way of exerting his independence. For as long as these associations were running in his mind, he was going to stay painfully thin even though he did want to put on weight and have a more solid body.

Monica's story was a little different. She and her single

mother had little money when she was a child. Her mother worked part-time and looked after Monica on her own. There was little money, even for the necessities. After a meal, her mother, conscious that she could not offer her more because the other half of the casserole was destined for tomorrow night's dinner, would say, "You don't want any more, do you Monica?" Monica knew that she was expected to say "No", and was rewarded with a smile and a hug. When she was old enough to look after herself in the afternoon, her mother worked full-time and there was more money. But the habit was so ingrained that Monica still ate only small meals. When she was offered more, she still said "No" and stayed painfully thin. By this time, being thin was somehow a statement that she was not selfish and that she was a thoughtful and caring child.

As an adult she felt guilty when she said "Yes" and ate more and pleased with herself and self-righteous when she refused it and said "No". Although, by now, being slim was not consciously associated in her mind with being unselfish and putting other people's needs ahead of her own. For Monica, learning to say "Yes" and to accept food was a necessary step to gaining weight.

So, as you can see, these two small words that may have been your masters is the past can now become servants of the future. Use them as tools to express your real needs and the real decisions of the moment. In relation to food, be sure that you know what real need is.

CREATIVE MIND POWER

We have spoken before of the power of your mind. If you think you look terrific, you relax and bask in other people's admiration. If you think you are a failure, you will create situations in which you fail. If you think you are happy, you are and if you think you are sad, so you are, too. Chances are you are very much better, more popular, more capable, more everything than you think you are, but you let your negative beliefs pull you down. In other words, you are not what you think but what you think you are. Work that one out.

Your life is framed by your beliefs. When I first started in practice I took people at face value, believing the outward picture that they presented. I got many surprises. An elegant well-dressed woman looking supremely confident exposed herself as an unhappy woman, afraid she would embarrass her successful husband. A beautiful would-be model came in, convinced she was fat and ugly and would never get a job. She didn't. But she could have done so had she believed in herself. There are people in jobs for which they seem to have no aptitude. You wonder how they got there and how they have stayed there. Often it is their solid belief in themselves.

Write a list of your beliefs about yourself. Include the things you commonly find yourself saying and what you think people say or think about you. Go back in time and recall what was said about you in the past as many of these may have now become part of your belief system. Then find a close sympathetic friend you can trust and who knows what you are doing. Ask them to comment on your beliefs and you will find differences that will surprise you. Then, list the beliefs you would like to have about yourself and make them into affirmations.

Lawrence, who was fifty and overweight, did this. He believed that he was fat and would always be fat, that he couldn't stick to a diet, that he had reached the top of his profession, that the fun had gone out of his marriage, that life was downhill from here on and that he would probably have a heart attack, just as his father had done.

He turned this list of negative beliefs into positive aspirations such as, "I am rapidly returning to the weight I was at thirty", "My life is moving into a new exciting phase", "I'm fit, well and healthy and choose to live a healthy life-style". He repeated these to himself so frequently and so convincingly that they all came about. He lost weight, was promoted into senior management, found new interests to share with his wife and his cholesterol level and blood pressure came down — all good signs for his heart and his health.

PERCEPTUAL FILTERS

All your beliefs have passed through perceptual filters. If a policeman at the scene of a traffic accident asks ten witnesses what they saw, the chances are that he will get ten different stories with definite contradictions. What you see is what you expect to see.

These filters include generalisations, deletions and distortions. One witness may have seen several accidents caused by speeding and generalised the assumption that *all* accidents are caused by speeding and will tell the policeman that the car was speeding. The woman who never notices flashing indicators will have deleted this and tell the policeman that the other car didn't have its indicator flashing. A third elderly person who thinks the young are troublemakers will claim that the young driver was trying to show off.

Firstly, we will take generalisations. If you go out without an umbrella twice and it rains twice, what happens? You soon find yourself saying "Everytime I go out without an umbrella, it rains". You have generalised two events into a belief system. Listen to the chatter you hear around you and make a mental note of all the generalisations you hear. These include such phrases as, "Every time I do the washing, it starts to rain", "Every time I get dressed in a hurry, I ladder a stocking" and "Every time I want the car, my wife has left it without petrol", and many more. Listen to other people's generalisations and listen to your own.

Next, there's deletion. Your boyfriend and you have been arguing a lot and you are beginning to think he doesn't care. Do you remember all the great things he did for you? No. These are deleted as you tell him he *never* does anything to help. You go to three cocktail parties at which you know no-one and can't think of a thing to say. You have been to others in which you joined in and had fun but they are lost in the embarrassment of the latest three and you find yourself saying you've never been any good at cocktail parties. Listen to yourself when you make a statement. Then ask yourself if this really is true all the time or if there are exceptions. You may say "I'm no good at sewing" and then remember a time when you made something success-fully. You may say that no-one gives you presents you like but then remember a great present you got recently. You may be falling out with your lover, having an argument, and saying he's stopped caring, conveniently forgetting the ten-derness he has also shown.

Finally, there's distortion. That includes such things as being given a present and wondering why the other person feels guilty or wondering what they want you to do for them. It may be harder for you to detect distortions than to detect generalisation and deletions. You may need help from a friend. Share this idea with them and explore some of your conclusions. Even if you still think your interpretation of an event is correct, try to come up with some other possible interpretation and consider the possibility that your conclusion may be a distortion.

All these perceptual filters allow you to take the events of your daily life and fit them into what you have come to expect of yourself and your life. They allow you to prove your beliefs as you filter out things that don't agree with them. You can change this if you so wish. These beliefs have been set by your past. You can change them for your future.

The first thing to do is to discover them and then explore them. Are they serving you? Is it helpful to say you're no good at sewing? If not, tell yourself you are good at it and start to make that skirt you would like. If you have generalised a few failed attempts at sticking to a diet into "I'm no good at dieting", recall the days you did stick with your diet and generate that new belief. If you have claimed you can never gain weight no matter what you eat, you may find you have carefully deleted from your mind all the times you skipped meals. If someone intends to pay you a compli-ment and comments on the weight you have lost, do you distort this into a belief that they are surprised you've done it and don't think you can continue or that you don't deserve a slim figure?

You can make amazing changes when you explore yourself and remove the filters that stop you from seeing clearly into the future.

SELF-CONFIDENCE

To lose weight successfully and keep it off, you must have confidence that you can do it. If you doubt it, the temptations will be too strong. The expectation of failure will create failure. If you believe you will eventually break your diet, your subconscious is likely to suggest that you might as well break it now and eat that cream bun. Why forgo the cream bun if you are going to break your diet at some stage anyway?

To be successful and make a go of life, you have to be able to trust and rely on yourself. To become the weight you think you want to be, you must have the confidence in yourself that says you can do it. Relying on yourself does not mean that you stop sharing and caring for other people or that you become aloof and superior. It does mean that, when the chips are down, you must make your own decisions and live by them and not depend on others to make decisions for you. Most advice is free and is not worth it. Dependence upon another person loads an impossible burden onto that person. They cannot take responsibility for your life. Dependency becomes slavery by mutual agreement. If you rely on others you may be able to blame them when things go wrong but does that make things go right? Hardly. You had a better chance of deciding correctly what is right for you than they did. Learn to rely on your own ability to make decisions that are best for you.

Be confident enough to make your own decisions. Affirm to yourself that you have the ability to change your life, to lose weight, to become slimmer, or to gain weight and develop your body. Affirm that it is no-one's doing but your own when things don't turn out the way you want. No-one can let you down if you haven't been leaning on them. You can ask for advice and other people's opinions, but treat it as just that — other people's opinions. Add it to your decision-making process if you wish but, ultimately, make your own final decisions.

COMPARISONS

There is no need to compare yourself to others because you are as you are meant to be. Comparing yourself to other people can lead to the conviction that you are not good enough because everyone, in some way, will have an attribute with which you can compare yourself unfavourably.

Maggie was always comparing herself to others. Her hair wasn't as lovely as Sue's. She wasn't as tall as Ann or as slim as Pat. Betty had a better nose, Barbara a better mouth. Jenny was more clever, Jane was more fun and Diane was more successful. Such comparisons can only lead to despair and disaster — nor are they valid. You can also do the reverse: you can always find some attribute of yours that you think is preferable to another person's. You could say you were funnier than Fiona, more helpful than Yvonne, and so forth, but people rarely do it that way.

Build up your self-confidence and stop seeking praise from other people. If you are trying to lose or gain weight to look better and no-one comments on your altered weight and improved looks, what do you do? Have a cream bun or refuse to eat as a consolation prize? If you change your weight because *you* want to then your own praise is praise enough.

Do you feel that by being slimmer you will look better and be more popular? Many people do. In the clinic it is common to hear such stories as Diana's. She came in determined to lose weight. When asked why, she explained that she was afraid her boyfriend was losing interest in her and becoming interested in a much slimmer woman. She was sure if she could lose weight she would win him back.

Robin was an athlete, she was very slim and her latest boyfriend had been commenting on the lovely curves of a mutual friend. Convinced he would like her better if she was heavier, she obediently set about gaining weight.

This is sad, for it equates you to the way you look and assumes you are liked for your external appearance only.

If you can become more self-confident and self-assured, if you can learn to accept and love yourself the way you are, and this doesn't preclude wanting to grow and develop and achieve more, you have a much better chance of creating a present and future that you will enjoy. You can never be better than you think you are. Other people may think you are, but *your* experience will be based on what *you* think you are. It is time to start thinking of yourself more highly.

You can practise building your confidence but do it in small steps. No-one ever learned to speak a foreign language, a new sport or mastered a new profession in one day. It is the same with developing your self-confidence and achieving your weight goals.

Decide that for the day ahead you will stay with a pre-set eating programme. Do this for just one day. Don't think or worry about the many days and weeks ahead: just focus on one day. At the end of the day recognise your achievement and acknowledge yourself. Perhaps you stuck to the programme rigidly. Well done! Perhaps you cheated a little bit but it could have been much worse. Well done! Give yourself a reward — but not food!

Instead of focusing on all the things you can't do, think about the things you can do. Make a list of these. List all the big things and the smaller things as well. You should be able to fill several pages with the things you can do. List everything from being able to tie a bow to wash the dishes, from driving a car to counting your change in the shops. You will find there is an amazing list of things you can do.

A woman who came to see me recently had five children, all happily married, and seven grandchildren. She had reared them and educated them well, in spite of limited funds. She had a successful business, looked after her home herself, supported an elderly aunt in a retirement centre and found time to baby-sit her grandchildren. She had done this in spite of problems in her marriage and a lack of formal school training. Yet when we dug a little below the surface, we came up with her own belief that she was worthless if she was not doing things for other people. She believed she would only be loved and liked as long as she kept helping others and that no-one would love her for herself. This had even become a major driving force in her life. Her way of dealing with this was to become so over-weight that her health was seriously affected. Once she had sufficiently rebuilt her self-esteem, she could lose the excess weight, and begin to believe that people would love her for herself and not for what she did. She could now dare to relax and let other people cherish her.

Go back to the list of things you can do and apply the television technique. Just as in the section on Guilt you played with your internal television, do the same here, too. Apply the television positively to all the things you can do and apply it negatively to those that you can't. In this way you will be able to let your confidence and self-esteem grow.

In a world where we seem to be preoccupied with not being conceited, it is hardly surprising to find most people actually have, deep down, an unrealistically poor opinion of themselves and their worth.

LOVING YOURSELF

Now and for your future it is time to learn to love yourself. With no thought of boasting or arrogance, you can tell yourself that you are a wonderful person, that you love and cherish yourself and that you deserve the best of everything and that this includes the figure you want.

In the section on Goals you will be told to find photos of yourself at the appropriate weight and with the figure you want and to put them where you can see them often. Each time you see these photos, acknowledge the person there, saying "That's me. That's the way I'll soon look and I deserve to". As well as acknowledging your ability to look that way soon, look at the person in the photo with love.

Many people avoid looking at themselves in the mirror. A

number of patients have told me that they only ever look at a part of themselves. They look at their hair when they are doing it, at an eyelid when they are putting on eye shadow, at their cheek when they are shaving, to see that their clothes are sitting correctly. But they still don't look at *themselves*.

Look at yourself clearly. Just as you can love people without liking everything they do and say, so, too, you can love yourself without necessarily approving of every aspect of what you see. You may indeed decide that right now you are overweight or underweight; you may decide that definite changes are needed. At the same time, do be conscious of loving that inner person and wishing the best for them.

YOUR BODY

We have talked elsewhere about doing things to please your body. In that context it was to give you something to do instead of eating, and was aimed at you if you are someone who eats when you are bored or want to put off the next task. Now it is to remind yourself that you are important and that you deserve to be loved and pampered.

Set aside some time each day to pamper yourself. What's that, you are thinking? You don't have time? That it would be selfish? Run the phrase "A way I feel about pampering myself is . . . ".

When Marian did this her list of completions included ". . . I'm too busy", " . . . I haven't the time", ". . . it would be selfish", ". . . the children need me", ". . . it would be wrong", " . . . I wouldn't get everything done in time". She was, in effect, telling the world that her children, her friends, her husband, her family were all more important than she was. I persuaded her to give it a try and she agreed, with some apprehension, to spend one hour a day doing exactly what she wanted. She would read a book, chat with a friend, spend time in the garden, sunbathe, have a massage, do whatever she felt like doing at that time.

As soon as she started doing this, other things came to light. At first she felt guilty. To some extent this interfered with her pleasure but she persevered, having committed herself to doing it. At the end of the hour she felt the need to get going and catch up, so in the rest of her day the things she had to do were done more quickly and more efficiently than before. Best of all her family started to comment on the changes. The big change they noticed was that she was no longer as irritable. The hour of personal pleasure she took for herself each day lifted her spirits. It was an oasis for herself. Whereas before, the entire day had been spent doing things for others, and she had begun to feel resentful and tense, now, she knew that she cared, that she had her private time, that she would have fun as well as do her job.

Taking the time to love and pamper yourself and showing the world that you do so is an important part of achieving your goals. Not only do you benefit, but so do the people around you.

THE MIRROR TECHNIQUE
All you need for this is a mirror and a bit of privacy.

Look at your image in the mirror and say "I love you". The nice thing about doing this is the image will say the same thing back to you. When you first start you will find yourself wanting to brush your hair, remove some dirt or smooth out a wrinkle. Don't do it. Look eyeball to eyeball so you get your message across to the inner self behind those eyes in the mirror.

You may feel strange and silly at first but persevere. In time, you will feel comfortable and you'll become aware of your self-esteem growing.

CARDS
Another useful trick when trying to change your self-image is to write messages for yourself. Put them on cards and leave them where you often look, such as in drawers, on your desk or in your car, even in the fridge.

Useful messages are:

I love myself unconditionally.
I'm terrific.
This is a great day and all is going well.
I'm in control and I choose to be happy.
This is my day.

You can make up your own message, as long as it gets the desired result.

AFFIRMATIONS

We have already talked about affirmations. See page 81 in the Tools section. This is an important point at which to use them. Remember there is no set list of affirmations. You do not need permission or authority for their wording. They can be as causal as you like. Just make sure you are always making positive statements about yourself.

Remember, too, that the affirmations can be as simple as "I'm great", "I'm good", "I'm terrific" or they can be more specific such as, "I'm rapidly reaching my ideal weight". One woman's affirmation was "I'm slimming".

Whatever you do, stop a negative thought as soon as you're aware of it. If you find yourself about to say "Oh, I'm hopeless" and are aware of what you are doing after "I'm h . . . " switch it to "I'm happy" and let the other thought fade. As in all things we have discussed, do not feel guilty about what you nearly did, or even about what you did. Don't make yourself wrong, beat yourself up and blame yourself. Praise is in order for catching yourself, at whatever point you do catch yourself, and for changing it around into something positive.

Make a special effort to speak only of positive and happy things. Next time you are in a group of people be aware of the number of negative stories recounted. You'll hear all those "You'll never guess what happened to me on the way to the theatre" stories and about the bad traffic, the queues, the nasty comment someone made. Less often you will hear about good things that happened. Sometimes we criticise the press for only publishing the bad news, yet we get what we ask for and enjoy, often we do the same things ourselves.

Before you open your mouth in future make sure that what you are going to say is positive. Talk only about the good things that happen to you. This will improve your self-image. If you talk only about the nice things that were said to you, you will feel better about yourself.

As you come to recognise that you create what happens to you, you will be less likely to comment on negative things, after all, why would you tell the world that you created problems for yourself?

Again, you don't have to believe this, you only have to do it. As soon as you do it, you will feel yourself beginning to change. Take the weather, for instance, there are no bad days. Rainy days are good for the garden, sunny days are good for sunbathing. Either way, you are stuck with the weather the way it is, you can either feel good about it or not. There are no obstacles to what you want to do, no difficulties, only challenges from which you will learn and benefit.

You *can* decide to feel good about yourself. It seems silly to choose to feel bad, doesn't it?

In the earlier part of this book you learned about yourself and your past. In this section you have been shown many different ways to create a body that is the shape you have been asking for.

We have talked about the things in your past that hold you back and shown you ways to let them go. These things will include many that are specific to you, such as your relationship with a particular person, your earlier habits, beliefs and so forth. We have also discussed such emotions as self-pity and guilt. You will have learned how you feel about saying no. And also about the instances when you say no when you mean yes and yes when you mean no.

The single most important thing you will have done is to start feeling good about yourself. Learning to love yourself, even if you do want to change, will increase your self-confidence.

All these things take time. It took a long time to get you to where you are now. It will take some time to change. The good news is that the change can take place just as fast as you want if you want it badly enough. All you have to do is to start creating the changes using the tools and the exercises you have been given here. Then it's a case of "Watch out future, here I come".

P A R T   S I X :
PRACTICALITIES

GOALS

Having come this far you have learned a lot about your past. Now, the time has come to decide just where you want to be and then to set out on the journey. Firstly, decide precisely on your goals and write them down. Just thinking about them is not enough. You need to have them written down and dated so you can refer to them easily and so you won't ignore them. Having a written record also enables you to mark your progress. It is all too easy to put aside those you have achieved, concentrate on the ones you haven't and call youself a failure.

It is rather like the patient who came into the office with ten complaints. They came back a fortnight later insisting that they had done everything that was asked of them and yet there had been no improvement. When you check on the complaints one at a time, you find that eight have gone completely, one is partially better and only one is as bad as ever. This remaining problem, however, has become the focus of attention.

In the first session with Yvonne she gave the following as her list of goals. She wanted to lose 12.5 kilograms (2 stone) and to come down to dress size twelve. She also wanted to be able to run for a bus, and for her looks to meet with her husband's approval. She wanted to be able to feel comfortable on the beach in a swimsuit and she wanted to be able to touch her toes. Three months later she was getting disheartened because she had only lost 9.5 kilograms (1½ stone). When we checked on the goal list that I had in her file (she hadn't kept one herself) she found to her surprise that all the other initial goals had been meet. Realising this gave her spirits an enormous lift and she was able to complete her weight loss with more ease.

When you articulate your goals, be accurate. Goals must be specific, measurable and *only just* achievable. They must be *only just* achievable because, if you make them too easy, you will have achieved little, have little sense of satisfaction, and not feel suitably rewarded for your effort. How would you expect to feel if you were 19 kilograms (3 stone) overweight and decided that your goal was to lose 2 kilograms (4 pounds), got there and felt much the same. Stretch yourself; go for the biggest goal possible but still be realistic. If you are tall and big-boned, there is no point in setting your sights on being short and petite.

Goals must be measurable. When you convince your subconscious that you want to lose weight and your goal is exactly that, then your subconscious will feel happy when you have lost only a couple of kilograms. You must specify exactly how much you want to lose. Then, consider the measurements you can expect to be when you are that weight, for your bust, waist and hips. Write these figures down too.

Next, consider the time it will take. When do you want to be this new weight? If you have chosen to lose 19 kilograms (3 stone) and plan to do it in a fortnight, this is unrealistic. If you want to lose 3 kilograms (half a stone) and set yourself three months, you are too easy on yourself.

Let's say you want to lose 20 kilograms (3 stone). You may assume you will lose 1 kilogram (2 pounds) in a week. To lose a total of 20 kilograms (42 pounds) will take twenty weeks. Be tough on yourself and set a goal of nineteen weeks. Make a chart of the proposed weights you will be at the start of each week. Your mind can then take over. By doing this, you have short-term goals as well as long-term goals.

Barbara found this technique to be one that made all the difference in her weight-loss programme. In the past, whenever she had lost a few kilograms, she had felt she could afford to eat a little bit more. After all, she rationalised, she was losing weight and was lighter than she had been. She kept focusing back on her starting weight, feeling good and permitting herself extra food, believing she had some leeway. When she drew the graph, she compared her weight each day, not to her starting weight, but where she had expected to be on that particular day. Instead of saying

"Mm, 67 kilograms, I was 73 when I started, I can afford to eat a little more", she said "Mm, 67 kilograms, that's about where I should be today according to the graph. I'm on track and will continue with my present eating pattern."

Make sure the goals are your goals and not someone else's. If your partner, parents or friends keep urging you towards a certain weight but you think you are fine as you are, then forget it. By trying to diet down to someone else's idea of what you should be, you are setting yourself up for failure. Only if you, yourself, want to be a certain weight, can you hope to reach it successfully.

The goals must be specific. Wanting to look better is too vague a goal. You must define exactly what you want or you will never know when you have achieved it. You must specify the changes you want. Do they refer to weight or size or to the clothes you can wear? Be specific and give yourself a definite target at which to aim.

Now, that you have set your goals — visualise them. Close your eyes. Picture yourself at your target weight. See the clothes you can wear. Picture your movements when you are slim. Do everything in your power to make this visualisation real. Make sure you see the end result, not as you are now or as you will be partly through the weight-loss process. Do not see yourself struggling to say "No" to food. Visualise only the glorious *end* result.

But do not stop here. Why do you want to lose or gain weight? If it is to be healthier, then this, too, becomes part of your goal. See yourself the picture of health. Have an imaginary conversation with your doctor or naturopath in which you are told how fit, well and healthy you are. Make clear pictures of all the things you can do with your new strength, suppleness and improved health. If part of your goal is to be more attractive and popular, picture yourself the life of the party. If it is to have a new lover, then picture that. Again, be specific, get a clear picture of just what this new you will be like.

While you are creating these visual images, consider your other senses as well. Be aware of how you will feel in this desirable future, the emotions you will have, how you will relate to people and the warmth you will feel. Hear the compliments as people comment on your slim figure. (Check with the section on Visualisations to make sure you are creating this picture as fully as possible.)

All this is part of setting goals. Write them down. Make them specific and measurable and *only just* achievable. Be able to see them, hear them and feel them. Commit to achieving them and you are on your way.

If possible, find a photo of someone about your height and the weight you would like to be. This can be a family photo or it can be a photo from a magazine. It can even be a photo of yourself when you were younger and slimmer. Cut the head out and replace it with a current photo of you as you are now. Put this where you will see it frequently during the day and keep this composite photo clearly in mind. Convince your subconscious that this is the person you really are temporarily hiding in an overweight body. It should then be a simple task to excavate that person and reveal it with the unwanted weight peeled away.

Once you have this goal clearly in sight and in mind, you are unlikely to want to overeat to revert to the fat you. You will begin to think and act automatically like a slim person. This is why it is so important to write your goals down and have a clear picture of them in your mind to look at.

Do exactly the same thing if you are underweight. Make up the appropriate photograph of yourself. Then convince your subconscious that this is the person you really are and it's just that your body is temporarily too small and some of it is temporarily missing. It is then a simple task to fill out the image you hold in your mind.

If you are too thin, with your new image in mind you will make it easier to eat a little more and to digest and absorb food in a more beneficial way.

SECRETS

Many people get so enthusiastic about their goals that they rush out and tell everyone about them, thinking that, by so doing, they are in some way making them real. Some people spend so much time and energy talking about their goals that they dissipate them and feel that they have already done enough. Don't do this. Keep your goals a secret to yourself. Just work quietly towards them.

It is estimated that as much as 48 per cent of women are on a diet at any one time and that 95 per cent of the population diets at some stage in their life. The chances are good, therefore, that if you share your weight-loss goals, the person to whom you are talking is also on a diet or thinks they should be. If you are doing well and they are slipping, they are likely to sabotage your effort. Unconscious of what they are doing, they will say such things as "Oh go on, just a small piece of cake can't hurt you", or "This is a holiday, give yourself a break and enjoy yourself. You can diet again tomorrow". They will feel threatened if you are succeeding. Alternatively, if they are losing weight faster than you are, you may feel disheartened even if you are on target with your own weight-loss programme.

Another person can also sabotage your efforts even if they have no intention, or no need, to lose weight. Tom came in to see me because he had been told to lose weight. His weight wasn't something he had given much thought to in the past. Nor had he given much thought to his meals, simply eating what was cooked for him. For the first two weeks Tom lost weight but then the weight-loss stopped. I asked him what he was doing that was different but he assured me there had been no change. He had given up the fried foods and cut down on the starches such as pasta and rice.

When this happens, I usually get the person to write down everything they eat and drink for a week. When Tom did this, I saw that he was eating fattening desserts such as apple pie, meringues and ice cream, trifle and rich custards.

Tom agreed that this was a bit unusual as there was mostly fruit or fruit salad for dessert. He was told to stick to fruit for dessert.

All went well for another week or two but then the weight loss stopped again and he actually gained a couple of kilograms. Checking up this time, his chart showed that his wife was now making a lot of rich sauces to go with his main course. It was time to talk with her. The result surprised all three of us. She was slim. It seemed, at first, unlikely that she would mind Tom losing weight. However, she did eventually admit to feeling stressed when he lost weight and we discovered that she had an underlying fear that if he got slimmer, other women would find him attractive. She hadn't been consciously aware of the way she was sabotaging his weight loss by making all her special desserts and then by choosing to cook main meals with rich sauces.

Once we worked that out and set about dealing with her fear, she was able to cook Tom the sort of low-calorie meals that helped him to lose weight, become healthier and, ultimately, be with her for longer than might otherwise have been the case.

For the chronically thin person gaining weight is probably harder than losing weight is for the overweight. Thin people are in a minority so it is wise not to talk about how much weight you plan to gain. Remember that nearly 50 per cent of the people you talk to will be on a diet or about to go on one. They are likely to have little sympathy with your problem. They may tell you to stop worrying and not to bother. All this may only weaken your resolve and your determination at a time when you need it.

For both overweight and underweight, there is yet another reason for keeping quiet about your weight goals. Unless your listeners are aware of the power of their own minds they may not be in tune with what we have already discussed. They might laugh when you tell them what you are doing and how you are doing it. Think back to your own skepticism when you started reading this book. Even without realising it, their criticism or comment may make you doubt yourself. This, in turn, weakens the energies you are bringing to bear on your changed emotions and thoughts. It slows down your process of delving into yourself and unearthing the reasons for your behaviour patterns and can hinder you in your path to your goal.

Make your goals and make them clear and specific, but then keep them to yourself. Make them your secrets. There is more on this in the section on Dos and Don'ts.

CHANGES

Let's now consider what happens to your body when you start to lose weight. It is also time to consider those plateaus, when, after a period of weight loss, you stay the same weight even though you are eating less and feeling positive.

All things considered, we are pretty conservative and not too keen on change. Our bodies are pretty conservative, too. For the purpose of this exercise, think of yourself as consisting of Body and Spirit. With all the changes you have been making to Spirit, give some thought to Body. So far Spirit has had all the attention.

Whenever, in the past, you chose to lose weight, there was instant conflict between Body and Spirit. Spirit made the decision to change but Body saw little reason to go along. With your new found tools, Spirit may be more eager than ever to change your weight and may be more powerful in its ability to do so. Body has yet to be convinced and may be feeling somewhat apprehensive.

After all, Body did only as it was asked, when you overate. It built all those cells and the complicated structure that goes with them. Every time you ate extra food it created more connective tissue scaffolding. Within each cube of this scaffolding, it partitioned off sections and within each section it created thousands of new adipose tissue or fat cells. It then filled these cells with fat that came either directly from food you ate or indirectly from the conversion to fat of excess starches and sugars you ate.

Body looked at its handiwork and it was pleased. It had created neat rows of fat cells all full or nearly so, all neatly stacked and organised by connective tissues and all of them ready to donate fat as needed elsewhere in Body for energy. Every time Spirit says Body must skip a meal, Body is able to spare a little fat from these cells to provide energy until the next meal. To make up for this, at the next meal Body makes sure that it sends strong messages to Brain so that extra food is provided to top up these partially empty cells.

Body sees no reason to change. It's done all the work so why destroy these cells. Besides, it's been here before. It knows that after a period of dieting, just as it has finally agreed to breaking up some of the scaffolding, getting rid of the sections and destroying the cells, Spirit will suddenly decide to overeat again and then Body will have nowhere to put the fat so it will have to start rebuilding again.

There's also an interesting conflict between two sub-parts of Body, namely Muscle (a dispersed entity comprising all the various muscles in your body) and Fat (another dispersed entity made up of the all the fat cells). Body seems more conservative with regard to Fat than it does with regard to Muscle. One of its defensive responses to on-and-off dieting is to insist that Muscle helps to provide needed energy when you are dieting and that not all the work is left to Fat. Somehow, it seems to be easier to use Muscle than Fat. However, when you start eating again, it is easier to make Fat than Muscle.

It is Muscle that can burn up Fat. If you have no Muscle but a lot of Fat, Fat can no longer perform its role which is to be a fuel source for Muscle. This means that Body, overall, will become big and flabby but will not have enough energy to do what Spirit wants. Thus, for everybody's sake, Spirit should be strong and demand that Body does change, and that it does do away with a lot of the adipose tissue cells it has built to store Fat. Only when Spirit is persistent and insists on restricting food intake on a long-term basis, does Body finally succumb. The plateau is overcome and your weight can go on down.

Don't get disheartened if you lose weight in stops and starts because that is the way it is likely to be partly for the reason just given and partly for another reason that has to do with your internal biochemistry. When Fat is first broken down, it is turned into water and carbon dioxide. Carbon dioxide is all right as you can breathe it out but water is hard to eliminate and will hang around, hiding among the cells like an errant urchin. When, finally, there is too much of it, Body will become aware of the problem and take action to expel it. When this happens, it departs via the kidneys. Another plateau is overcome and your weight will take a sudden drop.

If you are trying to gain weight, the reverse scenario operates. Spirit dicates that there is an increase in the amount of food consumed. There is now excess Muscle and Fat but nowhere to put it. Body could start to build some more scaffolding and then fill it with more fat and protein cells in which to store the extra amounts that have been eaten. But in this case, too, Body has been here before.

Body knows that as soon as it goes to all the trouble required to do the extra building, Spirit, being impatient, will decide it is uncomfortable being so full and will start to slow down the eating. Then, all Body's extra effort to build the new scaffolding will have been wasted. Why should Body bother? Better to just ride it out, knowing that Spirit will soon return to the old undereating ways.

Again, be persistent. Continue to eat the extra food. Body will eventually realise that Spirit this time is serious. The necessary building will occur and your weight will go up. In this case, not only will extra fat cells be built but your muscle cells will also be built. The relative amounts of each will depend on the type of food you eat and the amount of physical exercise you do. The more muscle work you do, the more muscle structures (as opposed to fat structures) Body will build.

WEIGHT AND INCHES

It is valuable to weigh yourself from time to time to check progress and also important to measure your inches. Measure your bust or chest, your waist, hips and thighs. The reason for measuring inches, as well as weight, is that Fat is bulky and light compared to Muscle which is heavy and compact.

On a good weight-loss, there will be times when fat is being converted into muscle. At these times your weight may stay much the same or even increase slightly but your inches will reduce. If you only measured your weight, you could get disheartened. By measuring your inches, you know that the positive change is still in process. After all, although we talk about losing weight, it's not really weight you care about. If you could become several sizes smaller while you stayed the same weight, wouldn't it be OK? You want to *look* better, *look* slimmer. Few people are going to lift you to determine how heavy you are.

In addition to keeping up your spirits, the knowledge that your measurements are diminishing, even if your weight isn't assures you that weight loss will soon be easier again. This is because the new Muscle that is forming will be able to burn up Fat faster.

If you are trying to gain weight, then also measure your inches. You want to gain Muscle; you probably don't want to gain Fat. It may be slower to increase size by increasing dense muscle tissue rather than Fat that is bulky. However, Muscle has a shape and looks attractive, healthy. Fat is more shapeless and tends to hang in folds. It is less attractive, and, unless needed as an energy store, it is less healthy. You almost certainly want to gain weight to gain strength and an improved shape. Muscle does it.

POSITIVE THOUGHTS

Now is the time to list some positive thoughts about changing your weight. In the past you have thought, "Dieting! What a bore! But I simply must lose weight", or "Making the effort to eat more! What a bore! But I simply must gain weight". The idea now is for you to embrace the idea of decreased or increased eating with enthusiasm. If you can make this and similar changes in your thoughts and attitudes, the whole process becomes a lot easier.

Run the phrase "A good thing about dieting is ... " Include health benefits, social benefits and financial benefits, plus any and all the others you can think of.

Then run the phrase, "A good thing about healthy food is ... "

Next, list the positive things you can find to say about your body.

The next phrases to run are "A good thing about losing weight is ... " and "A benefit I will get from being slim is ... ". Although they are similar, you will find there are some differences.

If you are too thin and want to gain weight, change the phrases accordingly. Run phrases such as "A good thing about eating is ... ". "A good thing about gaining weight is ... " and " A benefit I will get from reaching my target weight is ... ".

When you have your list of completions, take some time to think about them. Focus them. Focus on all the benefits you will gain. Use the visualisation techniques again. Create in your mind the picture, the thoughts and feelings conjured up by these benefits. Focus on these at all times so that changing your habits in a way aligned with these goals will seem easy.

TIMES OF CRISIS

You have done everything recommended in this book. You have had success, lost some weight and reached a time of crisis. Suddenly, it is all too much. You have had it! You intend to *eat*, no matter what the cost. You get up from where you are sitting and start heading for the fridge, the food cupboard or the cookie jar. STOP!

You can eat what you want in a minute but first do this. Get out of your body. That's right — get out of your body and move up onto the ceiling. Imagine you are part of a television crew filming and commenting on the scene below. "Audience, there she is sitting down and looking pensive. Is she pleased with the weight she has lost. Is she feeling good about herself? Somehow, she looks restless. Oh, wait. She's getting up and heading for the kitchen. Don't tell me our heroine is going to eat when she has been doing so well. What's that? She's hesitating. Maybe she won't give in." Then pan back to earlier film clips where the determined heroine resisted all temptation. "Watch, audience, see how strong she can be, how committed to reaching her goal. See how effective her new thought patterns have been". Cut back to the present. "Now, what is she going to do?" With an audience watching your every move, are you really going to binge out?

DEPRIVATION

One unusual aspect of this new approach to weight loss is that you should never experience deprivation. You have formalised your goals clearly. You have made sure they are your own goals. You have understood all your sabotaging techniques of the past. If you truly desire more than anything to become your new target weight, then not eating something should be seen as a desirable and positive step towards reaching your goal — not as the loss of a chance to eat and enjoy the food.

If, foremost in your mind is the desire for the taste of food, then you can have it, but on one condition. Stop and review your long-term goals. If they are still your real goals, then check out how what you are about to do will serve them. If eating will not help you, then focus on that long-term goal of losing weight rather than on the short-term goal, the taste of food. By doing this, the desire to eat will reduced.

Remember what we said about willpower? It will not do the trick for you. You have to *want* to lose weight every step along the way. Being slim must be more important to you than eating that extra bit of food. If it is not, then perhaps it is time to review your goals again.

DOS AND DON'TS THAT RELATE TO FOOD

In view of what we have said so far in this book it may seem that all you need do to be the weight you say you want to be is to sort out the emotional tangles, disassociate food from all other aspects of your life and think positive thoughts so that you consciously create the new you. This is correct — that is all you have to do. However, it is actually a big order and, whereas, in time, you may be able to do it quickly and easily, right now while you are learning these skills, some extra help may make things go faster.

If you practise what is said below you will find, in time, that this, too, is part of the programme of retraining your thoughts and adding to the power they have to make you into the person you'd like to be physically and mentally.

No, we are not going to suddenly revert to diets, to lists of food you can and can't eat or to counting calories. This section is about some practical things you can do to get you on your way and make things easier until your mind power is so strong and your emotions so clear that your emotional and mental problems are resolved. Even then, many of these practicalities still make good nutritional and health sense and should be followed as part of your new lifestyle.

Notice that the things discussed below are practicalities relating mainly to the logistics of eating rather than to the nature of what you eat. You were promised "without dieting" when you started this book and, "without dieting" it will be.

Once you decide to lose weight and eat less, there are some Dos and Don'ts to consider. Some of these Dos and Don'ts have been mentioned before; some of them are new. They are all here because it seems appropriate to concentrate them in one place for you.

- Don't consider that you are on a diet. You have simply changed your thoughts about yourself and about food and have decided to treat your body differently. You either want to be slimmer, fitter and healthier in the future, or you want to gain weight and be fitter and healthier in the future. The eating pattern that you are now choosing is the new eating pattern you intend to keep from now on. The weight loss or gain will be an additional bonus but is not to be focused on every morning when you wake up and face the scales.

- Don't tell other people you are on a programme to change your weight.

  Mary and her husband left the city to live in the countryside where their social life would consist of entertaining and being entertained by several other couples. She knew that this would involve 3000-calorie dinners with rich desserts as each hostess vied to outdo the other. She decided the only way to deal with this situation and not gain weight was to tell people she could not and did not eat sweets. The first time she was invited out, she explained this to the hostess beforehand.

  When everyone else was facing rich trifles, apple pies and cheesecakes, Mary was given a platter with some cheese and crackers. At afternoon teas, where all the scones, cakes and biscuits were laden with sugar, she was expected to eat only a small cucumber sandwich.

In this way she was able to participate fully in their social life and yet remain slim. Had she said, "Oh no, I can't, I'm on a diet," there would have been endless arguments and persuasions. She would have faced, "But just a little won't matter" or "Just this once, give yourself a treat", or worse and most unfairly "But you're so slim, it won't hurt you". She was slim *because* she didn't overeat or indulge in a lot of sugary foods.

By doing it her way, she couldn't give in to temptation or her cover would have been blown. Not only would she have looked foolish, she would also have made her friends feel manipulated, so her protection strategy also made sure she stuck with it.

- Do re-train your friends. In a way this is an extension of the above Don't. It means letting your friends know that you actually prefer the less fattening foods you choose. It means convincing them you mean it when you decline a second helping. It means showing them that you really don't want nuts, pretzels and chips before the gorgeous meal you're anticipating, nor the bread roll and butter placed beside your plate while you order. It means declining ice creams in favour of an apple when you are at the beach in such a way that people believe this is your real preference. When you do this and make a habit of it, you start re-training your subconscious as well.

- Don't feed negative messages to your subconscious. Again, this is really an extension of the above Do. You may follow the above message to the letter, only to relax when you are on your own and tell yourself how much you would really love Black Forest cake. Respect your subconscious because it is still listening.

- Do you feed positive messages to your subconscious? As you look at the cake, picture all the fat cells it builds, the way it clogs your arteries, the tiredness you feel later as your blood sugar darts up and then falls in a heap. Add to this by verbalising such thoughts as "What awful heavy/fatty food" and imagine how you will feel weighed down and clogged up by it. This may not be easy at the start but with a little discipline it becomes automatic. Believe me, I've tried it.

- Don't eat the leftovers. If your attitude, when you see food left on someone's plate as you start to clean the dishes away is "What a shame to waste it", think about it this way. The food has been paid for nothing can alter that. It has been prepared and cooked and nothing can alter that. The person for whom is was intended is not going to eat it and has left the table and nothing can alter that. You have had your meal and have been satis-fied. Now, you can either eat it yourself and get fat or put it in the dustbin. Either way, it is not going to benefit anyone. If you eat it, it will certainly *not* benefit you. It isn't even as if by eating it you would eat less at the next meal. We all know that doesn't happen. The same applies even if it is food on your plate, either at home or at a restaurant. The price will remain the same. Stop when you have had enough. Don't eat the left-overs.

- Don't skip a meal. It is all too tempting to think you're not all that hungry and you'll be very good and skip this meal thereby hoping that this will make weight loss easier. There are several problems when you do this. Firstly, you almost certainly will be hungry at some time before the following meal is due. You will be so proud of yourself for skipping the earlier meal, you may well argue that you deserve a reward or are allowed a little something extra. The chances are you will indeed eat something that will not be in your best interest.

Rowena frequently skipped lunch because she was so busy during the day in her boutique. She argued that she wasn't really hungry, she didn't have time to stop, and by not eating she would lose weight. The problem was that by around three or four o'clock, she was both tired and hungry. She would then either duck out and get something from the shop next door, which sold sweets, or ask a friend, if one dropped in, to get her something, which was usually a cake. She couldn't understand why she didn't lose weight, insisting that she only ate two meals a day, and that the cake was only a snack and didn't count. I pointed out that her favourite cake probably had a lot more calories than a large salad with cottage cheese. She now takes salad for lunch, has more energy, and is able to fit into one of the new dresses she has been eyeing on the rack.

There is another disadvantage to skipping a meal. Each time you have a meal, you speed up your body's metabolism. Once you have finished eating there is a lag before the metabolism slows down to its resting state. During this time it will burn up more fuel than when it is resting. It's a bit like the way a fire burns up coal. If you want a lot of coal (calories) burnt, you pile it onto the fire at frequent intervals, encouraging a roaring burn (high metabolic rate). If you want to burn only a small amount of coal you damp the fire down with just a few coals and not much air and don't disturb it (slow metabolic rate). In your case, you want your body to burn up lots of food energy or energy from your body fat, so have small frequent meals.

- Do eat breakfast like a king, lunch like a prince and dinner like a pauper.

For working and social reasons, most of us have a light breakfast and lunch and a large dinner. This is not a good eating pattern, particularly for people who are trying to lose weight. It has been shown that losing weight or gaining weight from a given amount of food can depend on the time of day in which it is eaten. If you eat a small breakfast and lunch and a large dinner on the one hand, or eat exactly the same amount of food, as a larger breakfast and lunch and only a very small dinner, on the other hand, you could gain weight on the first regime and lose it on the second. This is true even though the amount of food eaten is the same in both instances.

If you have your largest meal late at night, when no further exercise is planned, where is it going to go? That's right, into the fat stores. You may be able to call on it in the morning but you are more likely to respond to hunger by eating a sugar bun for morning tea. If you eat your main meals for breakfast and lunch, you have that food to burn for energy throughout the morning and afternoon. Not only does this have something to do with the time of day you expend energy and the time you are resting, it also relates to the changing hormonal patterns that happen during daytime and night-time.

- Don't have even a single mouthful of one of your binge foods. If you know there are some foods for which you get cravings, don't be tempted to have just a taste. If you know that, once you start to eat it, you won't be able to stop, why start? Many people have food allergies. Many of these people actually become addicted to the foods to which they are allergic. That is, in part at least, why most people find they are allergic to their favourite foods. The allergens can affect the brain just like morphine. Leave them alone or your plans for the new slim you will go out the window. If you want to explore this further get some allergy tests done or a simple blood test can be done for a hundred or more foods.

- Don't eat standing up. For one thing it's not good for your digestion anyway and for another, it encourages you to overeat. Many people, women especially, find their eating downfall is while they are preparing food, for themselves or for others. It's so easy to be chopping up carrots and eat some, grating cheese and eat some; stirring a dish, and taste some, gazing at a bit of leftover meat after you have carved and eat some. Before you know it, you have had a meal just standing in the kitchen. If it is six o'clock and you are hungry, eat something. But make it a rule to put that food on a plate, get the appropriate utensils and sit down where you normally eat. If you don't have time to do this, don't eat.

• Don't eat in the kitchen. For the same reasons as above, don't eat while you are preparing food. If you must eat at a certain time, take it into the dining room. If you haven't time for that, don't eat.

• Do use smaller plates and utensils than normal. This way, eating takes longer since you put less onto a small fork than a large one. Your eyes are more easily satisfied when they see a full plate even if it is a small one. Your mind knows it has had a full plate of food. Your subconscious is more easily satisfied.

• Do snack when you need to but do it gracefully. Arrange a tray with a cloth, add flowers, lay it properly, take it somewhere quiet, sit down, relax and enjoy it. If this is not possible and you don't have time, don't eat.

Susan loved cooking. On Saturdays she would indulge in an orgy of baking and cooking, filling the tins and the deep-freeze with food for the coming week. Her husband Roger had developed the habit of wandering through the kitchen and just trying a biscuit, some pastry, a small cake. He was, of course, overweight, and he too ignored these snacks, saying he only ate three regular meals in the day, drank very little and couldn't understand why he was gaining weight. After talking things over with him and his wife it was agreed that they would have a sit down afternoon tea on Saturdays, at which he could try Susan's baking. A month or so later, Susan reported that the size of their Saturday evening meal had diminished considerably. Roger was now conscious of having sat down to a meal, the cakes and biscuits, only a couple of hours earlier and his mind told him that to have another full meal was gluttony, a light snack would do.

It's all too easy to think you can fool the subconscious into believing you haven't actually eaten when you slip the food quickly into your mouth as you are doing other things. But you can't fool your fat stores, they know they have been added to.

- Don't read a book or watch TV while you are eating. If you are overweight it's because you have eaten too much and presumably enjoy food, so be conscious of it when you eat it. Be aware of the colours, the aromas, the taste and the feel of it. Enjoy it while it is in your mouth — you don't have taste buds lower down. For the same reason chew each mouthful fifty times. You spend hours thinking about food, anticipating food, deciding what to eat, trying not to eat, so when you do eat, stop, savour it, enjoy it and make it last.

- Apart from everything else if you chew your food for a long time, you are likely to eat less. This is because it takes about fifteen minutes for food to get into the bloodstream and inform the brain and then give the brain time to register that you are no longer hungry. Eating slowly may also mean you run out of time to finish your meal. That is OK, too if you are trying to lose weight.

- Do allow for your habits and make the appropriate allowances and arrangements. If you love to sit down after dinner and nibble while you watch TV, prepare appropriate nibbles. Cut up fresh fruit and have some plain yogurt to dip the pieces into instead of eating sweets or chocolates. If you think you eat too much fruit this way, put it in the deep freeze first. There's a lot of sucking in one frozen grape and a frozen fresh date is a very delicious slow nibble. Try it.

The same goes for pre-dinner snacks if you like them. Dice up carrots, celery and green peppers, make a light herb dressing to dunk them in, arrange them attractively and nibble on these rather than on more fattening nuts and cheese biscuits.

There are also some special Dos and Don'ts if you are too thin.

- Do eat frequent meals. Even if they are a bit smaller than your three main ones, you are likely to eat more food this way. You are also likely to absorb a greater proportion of it.

- Do eat sitting down rather than standing up or walking around. Again this is because your digestive system will function better this way and you will absorb more of it.

- Do arrange food and make it look attractive. The digestive juices will be stimulated and digestion and absorption will be improved.

- The final Do and Don't. If you plan to stick to these Dos and Don'ts and occasionally fail, don't give yourself a hard time. Don't call yourself useless because you can never stick to a diet and always fail at everything, anyway. Do acknowledge yourself for all the times you have stuck to them. Do acknowledge yourself for recognising your slip, making it only a small one and getting back on your intended course of action. It could have been much worse.

DAILY DOS AND DON'TS

It is now time to look at some practical Dos and Don'ts that relate to things other than food. Being the weight you want to be is not just a matter of what you eat and when you eat it. Sorting out your emotions and thoughts is not done only in your head. The achievements that go on inside you will ultimately be reflected in your outward life. Your altered relationship with yourself will be reflected in richer relationships with other people. Changes will also occur in your way of living, in the many practical things you do each day and the way you treat your body. These too will reflect the way you feel about yourself.

These daily Dos and Don'ts will help you during the process of change and transformation. In the end, your improved physical actions because of conscious decisions to make appropriate changes will come together with your internal changes in a harmonious whole. Initially, you will follow many of both groups of Dos and Don'ts by conscious decision and discipline. In time, they will become automatic and reflect the inner changes that have taken place.

- Do be sure that everything you do is your choice. No-one else is making you lose or gain weight. No-one else is forcing you into this new regime. It is your choice and yours alone. You don't *have* to do this, you do it because you *want* to. What you weigh now is your choice. What you will weigh in the future is your choice. What you eat and what you drink and the amount you exercise is *your choice.*

- Do start with small and specific targets. If you are about to go out with friends for a meal, make some decisions on what you will do. Make the appropriate short-term goals. Decide ahead of time that you will have a tossed salad for entree and grilled fish and vegetables for the main course and no dessert. Then picture the evening ahead and see yourself eating these foods, nothing else, and enjoying them. Decide that you will have exactly one-and-a-half glasses of wine, and no more. Picture this too. Create in your mind the feeling of satisfaction you will feel when you return home with no regrets or self-recriminations about the amount you overate. Then, live the evening this way. Or if you are going home to have a meal on your own, picture the way you will lay the table, put out a flower, make yourself feel glamorous. Anticipate your feeling of pleasure and self-satisfaction afterwards. Then go ahead and live the evening this way.

Creating and achieving these short-term goals shows that you can do it. You can create long-term goals too, and live up to them and achieve your aims.

- Don't focus on what you are afraid you will do. Don't think about the dessert you fear will tempt you. Don't focus on how full you will feel after you have eaten it. Whichever scenario you think about most is the one most likely to eventuate. This is your choice.

- Do list all the ways other than those involving foods that give you pleasure. Relax in a bubble bath and then have a light meal. Create the good feeling this will induce and then live the evening as you have envisaged it.

- Do create a target image. Find an old picture, one taken when you were the weight you now want to be or make up that combination we spoke of earlier with your face on someone else's slim body. Make sure that everywhere you look you see a positive goal for yourself and reassure yourself that this new body shape is possible. This way you will start thinking of yourself as a slim person about to emerge rather than the fat person with whom you are not happy.

- Do pretend you are on TV. Imagine a documentary is being made of you and all the world is watching. Do you want them to see you sneak an extra cookie? Or do you want to look good to the audience in your habits and behaviour and appearance. If you are too thin do you want them to see how little you are eating, how you are rushing your meal, how little time you are prepared to spend nourishing your body?

- Do make a list of the positive attributes of your body. These might include the colour of your hair or eyes, your smile, your ankles. List every possible compliment you can pay to yourself about your body and put these lists everywhere. Concentrate on what you like about yourself, not on what you don't like. This way you can start to really feel good about yourself and when you do, changing your weight is a lot easier.

- Do surround yourself with slim people, people who look the way you would like to look. You may think you are less conspicious in a crowd of either fat (if you are overweight) or very thin people (if you are underweight) but is this where you want to be? If everyone you see has the sort of figure you are trying to be rid of, you will continue to feel the same way and change will be that much more difficult. If you are overweight and surround yourself with fat people you also acquire the habits of fat people, and the biggest and most detrimental one is the habit of overeating. When you are among slim people you start to think like a slim person. You start to acquire the attitudes and habits of a slim person. Food and dieting will be less of a talking point. You will automatically eat and drink less, as they do. If you are underweight and surround yourself with skinny people who are uninterested in food, it will be that much more difficult to gain weight.

- Do please your body. Many people eat for comfort but

you can comfort yourself with other bodily pleasures. Many people eat out of boredom but you can fill your time with pampering your body. Many people eat to put off doing something else. Use the same time to take care of your body Arrange to have a massage, a facial, a manicure. Get your hair done. Do similar things at home. When you feel the urge to nibble, do your nails, deal with the hair on your legs, rub yourself with body lotion, pluck your eyebrows, give yourself a facial. Not only will this stop you eating and enable you to look slimmer, your general appearance will also improve and so will your image of yourself. This, in turn, will make it easier to eat the appropriate foods.

Many, if not all, these suggestions can be used by men as well as women, although men are forgiven for having hairy legs.

- Do buy some new clothes as your weight starts to come off. It is disheartening to be losing weight still wearing old clothes and feeling much the same. Buy only one or two outfits, as you are still on the way down and they, too, will soon be too big for you. Alternatively, concentrate on accessories first, new shoes and scarves. Buy new underwear because it tells your subconscious you like and approve of yourself. If you have beloved clothes left in the wardrobe since you gained weight, get them out and get them ready to wear again as soon as you can fit into them. Spend time cleaning and mending them if necessary and check the accessories that go with them. Keep this as one of your targets.

  If your goal is to gain weight, you, too, will have to buy new clothes as your weight changes. Again, buy just a few until your reach your target weight as you will also outgrow them.

- Do live "as if" you are the weight you want to be. This helps to reinforce the new image you are creating.

- Do work with positive affirmations such as:
  I am rapidly reaching my ideal weight.
  I love these slimming salads and fish.
  I am in total control of the amount that I eat.
  I choose to be slim, taut and terrific.

OR

- I am rapidly gaining the weight I desire.
  My muscles are getting stronger every day.
  I now fully digest and absorb all the food I eat.

You have possibly read these Dos and Don'ts in one sitting. Now it is your turn to put them into action. Thought can be powerful and it is at its peak when it is converted into action.

EXERCISE

No, you don't have to exercise. You don't have to don running shorts and jog around the block, wobbling at every turn, or, if you're skinny, showing your knobby knees. You don't have to don a bikini and stagger out through the surf to swim the length of the beach. You don't have to take up a new sport, enrol in a gym and do hours of aerobics. Nor, to gain muscle, do you have to do press-ups, sit-ups or lift weights. You don't even have to walk up stairs instead of using the lift, walk to the corner store instead of taking the car, or park some way from your destination and walk the last few blocks. It just helps if you do.

Why do you dislike exercise so? There are some who enjoy sports, that like the feel of their body and enjoy its capacity to do what they ask it. But in spite of the popularity of the beach, tennis courts, gyms and keep-fit centres, such people seem to be in the minority. Even many of those that join gyms and aerobic classes don't enjoy exercise; they join to put in some discipline and having spent their money, they had better make use of it.

Even having the word for it such as "exercise", tells you that we do too little physical activity. Who would ask farm labourers, mountain guides, camel herders in the Sudan or the nomadic Australian Aboriginals in their native bush if they exercised? They spend their days in physical activity and it is part of their life as it should be part of yours.

Some people feel that a game of tennis or squash once a week is "exercise" and allows them to take the car to the corner store for the rest of the week. The best activity for your body is the sort that occurs on and off throughout the day. It means walking whenever you can instead of using transport. It means using the stairs instead of lifts. It means running or jogging instead of walking whenever you can.

Whether you want to burn up fat and lose weight or build up muscle and gain weight, exercise is only effective if you are breathing more deeply than usual because you are pulling in oxygen to burn up fat and generate the needed energy. Whether you lose or gain weight will depend on whether you fuel the exercise with your own body fat or the extra food you eat. Exercise, or being physically active, means puffing, sweating and making an effort by using your own horse power.

Deirdre said she didn't have time to exercise, she worked full-time and had to look after her flat. Later I asked her what she did in the evenings and was told "Nothing much, there isn't much to do really, unless I go out with friends". No time to exercise?

If you are seriously overweight, don't use the excuse that you don't have time. You may not have time not to. Lack of exercise can shut down a lot of your circulation system, clog up the arteries and seriously increase your chances of a shortened life.

Run the phrase, "The way I feel about exercise is .." and surprise yourself. Tracy did, she found herself saying exercise was "undignified" and "masculine". After some discussion she agreed that dancing was both graceful and feminine and enrolled in ballroom dancing classes. She "exercised" three times a week and made a lot of new friends.

Stop thinking of it as "exercise", as an activity on its own to be added to the list of things you have to do each day. Think of it instead as "activity" and include it in your day.

Terence ran the phrase "The way I feel about exercise is . . . " and got completions that included "shameful". "A reason exercise is shameful is . . . " produced "it means you have no money". In his youth there had been little money to spare. Terence and his brother lived in one of the outer suburbs of a large country town. The other children were either driven to school by their parents or caught a bus. Terence and his brother had to walk. By the time they arrived they were hot and dusty and usually in trouble for looking messy, all of which shamed them in their own eyes, not because as small boys they had a desire to be neat and clean but because it highlighted their parents' lack of money.

Terence swore that as soon as he had money he would not walk anywhere again. He saved up, first for a bike, then for a car. Now he drives even to pick up the paper from the newsagent a hundred yards away. Now that he understands his motives he has satisfied both his body's need to exercise and his mind's need to show wealth by enrolling in an expensive gym.

Many patients have told me they would walk more but that they always seem to be carrying something; they have too much to carry and so they have to use the car or bus. Secretaries have too many letters and parcels, housewives have too much shopping, travellers have too much luggage and sales reps have too many samples. Try those small luggage trolleys. They may be meant for suitcases but they are excellent for briefcases, heavy handbags, sample cases or the shopping. If the wheels run smoothly you can walk miles with them and you can even jog.

If your greatest exercise to date has been opening the fridge door, don't suddenly sign up for a marathon. Start slowly. Anything more than you did yesterday is a bonus.

Build it into your life gradually, a little at a time until it becomes second nature to you.

MORE HELPFUL ADVICE

As you will have discovered, this book is mainly about the emotional and mental side of losing weight. In addition, we have covered some practical things such as working out your goals and some practical Dos and Don'ts. Even now we are not going to discuss which foods you should eat and which foods you should not eat. However, it is a good idea at this point to add some positive and practical nutritional things you can do to make losing weight as easy as possible once you have settled on the eating pattern that you think is right for you.

ALLERGIES

If you are a binge eater, and find that once you start eating something, you can't stop or if there are certain foods for which you get cravings, you may find you are allergic to them. It is reasonable to wonder why a body would crave food that it reacts to allergically. The reason is that many allergens contain protein and the amino acid chains of the protein act on the opiate receptors in the brain, somewhat like morphine. No-one needs to be told how addictive morphine is. Allergens can also be addictive. Many people find that when they eat something to which they are allergic, they get a high, a sense of increased wellbeing, alertness and energy. This can result from the effect of the allergen on the adrenal glands which pump out adrenalin, giving you the burst of energy.

If you have any reason to suspect you have food allergies then have an allergy test done. A cytotoxic test for about a hundred of the most commonly eaten foods will give you a pretty fair indication of the foods you should avoid. Once you have your list of allergens, avoid these foods. Avoid them totally, do not let a crumb or a drop pass your lips. When you get over the first few days, the cravings go. From then on, provided you continue to eliminate these foods, it should be much easier to control the amount of other foods you eat.

SUPPLEMENTS

By supplements, I mean the vitamins, minerals, essential fatty acids and amino acids that *should* be in your diet but may not be in sufficient quantities. These are all the things your body needs to be fit and healthy provided that you also have an adequate supply of calories for energy. These energy calories are not a problem if you are overweight as stored fat gives you energy. The problems come when we consider all the other essential nutrients. Since these were not laid down in your adipose tissues when you laid down these fat stores, it follows that your body fat is a poor source of these essential nutrients. Supplements could be in order: if you are going to lose weight by eating less, and relying on your body fat for energy, it goes without saying that you will become deficient in vitamins and minerals. If you are under-weight, you are going to have to eat more than usual and so you will be getting more vitamins and minerals. However, you may still benefit from additional supplements since one of the reasons you are having trouble putting on weight may be that your body lacks some essential nutrients. It would be nice if your body could tell you specifically just exactly which nutrients it needs and in what quantity but this is not the case.

Brain may be clever and very articulate in many areas but it is extraordinarily limited in some forms of communi-cation. When it wants to communicate with Body regarding food, it has only two signals. The first is "Yes, that is sufficient. Stop eating." The second is "No, there are still some nutrients of which I have had inadequate amounts. Keep eating and let's hope you choose the right foods so I get all that is needed and we can both take a rest." Notice that Brain does not specify which nutrients have not been supplied. All you know is that Brain is signalling "hunger" and you eat some more. If, what you eat still does not provide Body with the correct nutrients, then Brain will leave the "hunger" sign on and you will overeat.

One way around this is to take some extra supplements. Take a good multi-vitamin tablet and a good multi-mineral tablet. Make sure you get sufficient essential fatty acids, either in capsule form or from good cold-pressed vegetable oils, nuts and seeds. If your digestion is poor, you may also benefit from an amino acid supplement, especially one that is rich in carnitine, the amino acid that helps get the fat into the cells and burned up for energy. This may be especially important if you are a vegetarian as it is found only in animal foods.

KELP AND YOUR THYROID

Some people have slightly sluggish thyroid glands. A lot more people *think* they have a sluggish thyroid. After all, it's much easier to blame a gland than to acknowledge that you chose to overeat! If you are wondering about the state of your thyroid, here is a simple test you can do.

Before you go to bed at night take a thermometer, shake it down and put it handy on your bedside table so that it is ready to use. First thing in the morning, while you are still in the process of waking up, put it under your armpit and go back to sleep for ten minutes. The idea is to take your temperature while you are as near as possible to the sleeping state. Just be careful you don't break the thermometer in the middle of whatever dream you fall back into. Repeat this for ten days. If you are female, avoid the days when you are ovulating. If this resting armpit temperature is consistently less than 36.5 C, your thyroid may be on the lazy side. This is a sensitive test and will pick up a problem even before it becomes obvious in blood tests. If your thyroid is sluggish it may need some kelp added to your diet. Kelp contains iodine which is what the thyroid needs to do its job.

There are also some homoeopathic remedies that will help to give the thyroid a boost. Since this can be done without over-stimulating the thyroid, there is little if any risk. Beware of the thyroid hormone, thyroxine, as a remedy because it can slow down the thyroid gland on a permanent basis. Do not try to persuade your doctor to prescribe it for you.

LECITHIN AND YOUR FATS

When you start to lose weight, you start to break up your stores of body fat. This means that, overall, you are using a higher than normal fat supply. This fat, from whatever you get in your diet and your fat cells, enters the blood stream, cycles throughout your body and has to be processed by the liver.

Lecithin, derived from egg yolks or soy beans, helps the liver in its task of managing your fat metabolism. Adding some of this to your diet as granules, powder or capsules can help the weight-loss programme along and can also help the liver in general, with other health benefits. You can boost this effect if you take a more general nutrient supplement aimed at helping the liver. It should contain several of the B group vitamins including vitamin B6, folic acid and vitamin B12, choline and inositol, the mineral magnesium and the amino acids methionine and taurine.

The amino acid carnitine helps your cells take in the fat that is passing by in the blood stream and to burn it up for energy. If you are deficient in carnitine, your cells may refuse to use the fats that are passing by in the blood stream. You will feel tired and, as a result, you will feel you simply have to eat something and you will sabotage the diet. In theory, your body can make carnitine and, in practice, it probably does. But if your body is a bit slower than average at making it or if you don't supply the necessary starting materials which include methionine, magnesium and B6, then you may not make it in sufficient quantities. Taking a supplement could help you to burn up your body fat, give you increased energy to lose weight.

Make sure that your diet is high in fibre. Dietary fibre is not absorbed. Some of it, while it is in your digestive system, also has the capacity to mop up fats and take them straight through the system and out of your body. This is the basis for using oat bran to try to reduce cholesterol levels. The oat bran mops up the cholesterol that is in the bile and prevents its re-absorption back into the blood stream. So eat oat bran, other cereal brans and lots of vegetable fibre.

Coenzyme Q 10 is another nutrient (you could almost call it a vitamin as it acts somewhat like one) that helps to improve fat metabolism. It is relatively new in the market place but is now available from health food shops.

AMINO ACIDS

Other amino acids, in addition to these mentioned above, are helpful. Tryptophan is converted into serotonin in the brain. This in turn decreases appetite and carbohydrate consumption. It stimulates the production of cholecystokinin which is a powerful appetite suppressant.

Phenylalanine, another amino acid, also stimulates the production of cholecystokinin. Tyrosine does the same and increases brown fat metabolism. Brown fat is the fat that is metabolically active and is capable of burning up other fat. White fat is relatively inactive, acting as a fat store rather than an insulator and heat generator.

Glutamine is a derivative of the amino acid glutamic acid. It works in the brain and helps to reduce your craving for sweet things. It can also reduce a craving for alcohol which can be a source of a large number of calories if you enjoy a few extra drinks in the day.

VITAMINS

The B group vitamins can help reduce your cravings for

sweet foods. If your sweet tooth remains a problem, increase your intake of these.

MINERALS

Chromium is an important mineral in the metabolism of sugar. Without it, the cells have trouble absorbing glucose from the blood stream. The result is similar to that obtained when you are short of carnitine and can't use fats for energy. Because they are not able to absorb the glucose from your blood stream, the cells cannot generate the energy they need and you feel tired, start craving more food and, horror of horrors, there goes your latest diet. Supplementing your diet with glutamine, chromium and all the B group vitamins can reduce your sweet craving considerably, thus reducing your inclination to binge on sweets, lollies, chocolates, cakes and biscuits.

FIBRE

Fibre was mentioned above in the context of mopping up fat in the digestive system. It also helps to fill you up and make you feel you have eaten more than you have and in this way helps you to eat less. It is excellent for the bowels and helps you to get rid of some of the toxins released in the weight-loss process.

Take a general multi-vitamin supplement and a general multi-mineral supplement. You won't get enough of everything into one tablet so take them separately. This will help to ensure that you don't get a "hungry" message from the brain because you're lacking a particular nutrient. As a guide the vitamin supplement should have 10,000 i.u. vitamin A, 100 vitamin E, 250 milligrams of vitamin C and around 50 milligrams of the major B vitamins. For the mineral supplement, get the strongest one you can. It still won't have all your daily needs as minerals are bulky but it will be a supplement to the minerals that, hopefully, are in your diet.

FOOD

Ideally, you should think of yourself as altering your eating patterns so they result in permanent weight change and better health.

For a general guide make a large proportion, as much as 75 per cent of your diet fruit and vegetables. The fruit should be eaten fresh and raw as should lots of the vegetables in salads or nibbles. Other vegetables should be lightly steamed. Include low-fat protein such as fish and cottage cheese. Eggs and plain yogurt have their place. Any grain or grain product, such as cereals and foods made of flour, should be brown or wholemeal. If you focus on vegetables rather than bread as being the central staple of your diet, you will find it easier to stay slim and healthy.

Avoid processed foods. That's a big one. All those packets of instant foods, tins of easy meals, bottles and jars of sauces and toppings and many more are a calorie bonanza and often a health hazard. Avoid fatty and fried foods, sugar and things made with sugar. Eat fruits rather than drinking their juices. Have herb teas rather than tea or coffee. Limit your alcohol intake to a sensible amount, and avoid the splits, the ginger ales and so forth as they pack a powerful punch of calories. Have a glass of dry wine rather than brandy and ginger ale.

If you are trying to gain weight, follow the above guide lines for they are still nutritionally sound and will give you the nutrients you need. Include some of the filling foods, raw nuts, whole grains, beans and lentils to help you gain the desired weight. Don't include high calorie unhealthy foods such as cream, fried foods and sweets. You want to gain muscle, not flab. Drinking fruit and vegetable juices is a good and compact way to take in a lot of calories and a lot of nutrients even if your stomach is feeling stretched to capacity.

MAKING IT HAPPEN

To achieve the final result, you will go through a number of stages. The first stage will be wishing to be your ideal weight when it is still a dream. Then the wish becomes strong and there is a real desire to be slim. After that you start planning. The next step is actually making the changes. The final step is having the end result and being the weight you want to be.

You go from wishing to wanting to planning to doing to having. Many people go through the wishing and wanting stages. Many people get to the planning stage. Fewer people start in on the doing. Still fewer reach the final stage.

I won't say "Good luck". When someone told a friend that he was lucky as he sunk a long golf put, he said, "You know it's a funny thing, but the more I practise, the luckier I get".

You now have the tools to do it and only you can make it happen.

INDEX